50 years of the Royal College of
Nursing in Wales 1!

G000055336

Nursing Matters

Greg Lewis

GRAFFEG

Royal College of Nursing in Wales 50 years
Published by Graffeg March 2016
© Copyright Graffeg 2016
ISBN 9781910862575

Royal College of Nursing in Wales 50 years
Author © Greg Lewis

Designed and produced by Graffeg
www.graffeg.com

Graffeg Limited, 24 Stradey Park Business
Centre, Mwrwg Road, Llangennech,
Llanelli, Carmarthenshire SA14 8YP Wales
UK Tel 01554 824000 www.graffeg.com

Coleg Nyrsio Brenhinol
Royal College of Nursing
Cymru • Wales

Contents

Foreword

by Professor Mark Drakeford AM
Minister for Health and Social Services

The history of the Royal College of Nursing in Wales is, in some ways, the history of devolution.

Tŷ Maeth was opened in 1965 and in that same year we heard the very first stirrings of devolution when Jim Griffiths became the first Secretary of State for Wales – the history of politics in Wales and the emergence of the RCN Wales goes hand in hand.

In the post-devolution era that relationship has become even closer. I meet the Director of RCN Wales every six weeks – we have a full agenda which we discuss between us. RCN Wales is a critical friend; it represents its members powerfully and it wants to make sure it makes a difference for its members by being willing to engage with government.

The very first week that I was Health Minister I spent a day with RCN Wales, going out on the wards, meeting people doing the job, talking to them and hearing from them. I've had opportunities to do that since in North, South, East and West Wales with RCN members – RCN Wales is fantastic at connecting me directly with people who are on the frontline of NHS Wales.

The RCN also has an all-Wales policy function. It responds to consultations and takes part in debates about important new directions for the health service. As well as sharing nurses' frontline experiences, it is also in a position to collect information from the wider Welsh nursing profession and turn it into a set of ideas, which it contributes to the rich mix of possibilities we have for designing the future of health and social services in Wales.

This is one of the toughest times in the history of the NHS. The cuts to our budget in Wales are massive; the demand for services is unremitting. People on the frontline find themselves at the sharp end of the pressures on the health service, while managing the impact austerity is having on their own lives. I never underestimate the impact this must have on people's working lives but whenever I meet nurses what comes through to me most powerfully is their sense of passion for compassionate patient care and their commitment to overcome the challenges we face.

Our nurses in Wales are determined to do the job in the way that they believe the job should be done – they believe in high-quality care for their patients, whether they are working in people's homes, GP surgeries, schools, local communities or our hospitals. Our nurses are forward-looking too – they are not just rooted in the ways things have always been done and they are prepared to look for imaginative solutions to meet healthcare needs, both old and new.

We are lucky in Wales with the nurses that we have working in our NHS. Our nurses are rooted in the life of the community; they are valued by their patients and by the public. RCN Wales represents this fantastic group of people with professionalism and a real sense of wanting to put the needs of patients first.

As we celebrate 50 years of RCN Wales, I think its future in the Welsh NHS looks absolutely secure. It is embedded into healthcare, the health service and health policy in Wales. It speaks with authority and it is listened to when it speaks. We don't always agree but that is exactly how it should be.

Royal College of Nursing in Wales Roll of Honour

RCN Welsh Board Secretaries and Directors

Hettie C Hopkins OBE 1963 – 1978
Anne Pegington OBE 1978 – 1998
Liz Hewett 1998 – 2004
Tina Donnelly CBE 2004 –

Chairs of the RCN Welsh Board

Noreen Thomas 1962 – 1963
Mary Jones 1963 – 1966
Noreen Thomas 1966 – 1969
Pauline Matthews 1969 – 1971
Edward J Lyons 1971 -1977
Alun I Giles 1978-1987
Megan Edwards 1987 – 1991
David Thomas 1991 – 1999
Eirlys Warrington 1999 – 2007
Gareth Phillips 2008 – 2009
Ann Taylor-Griffiths 2009 – 2011
Christine Thomas 2011 – 2013
Gaynor Jones 2013 –

RCN Fellows

1982 – Professor Dame June Clark DBE, PhD, RN, FRCN, FAAN, FLSW

1998 – Professor David Jones OBE, FRCN, Hon.DSc

2000 – Jill Evans OBE, FRCN

2003 – Professor Ruth Northway PhD, MSc(Econ), RNLD, ENB 805, Cert Ed(FE), FRCN

2004 – Professor Sue Bale OBE, FRCN, PhD, BA, RGN, NDN, RHV, PG Dip, Dip N

2012 – Professor Philip Burnard, PhD, FRCN

2013 – Professor Maggie Kirk, PhD, BSc Hons, RGN, Dip N, Cert. Counselling, SFHEA, FRCN

2013 – Professor Donna Mead, OBE, OStJ, FRCN

2015 – Denise Llewellyn FRCN

Introduction

by Tina Donnelly CBE TD DL
Director, RCN in Wales since 2004

This book provides an overview of the establishment of the Royal College of Nursing Headquarters in Wales, Tŷ Maeth. It is published as a commemorative account of the members of the nursing profession who have helped to make the Royal College in Wales the establishment it is today.

The creation of the book began in 2015 during the 50th anniversary celebrations of the opening of Tŷ Maeth. We are very grateful to the nurses who launched the fundraising programmes 50 years ago which led to the building of Tŷ Maeth.

The following pages provide information about the outstanding journey that Tŷ Maeth and the Royal College has taken over the past half-century in Wales. Given that during 2016 the Royal College of Nursing will also celebrate their Centenary, '100 years as a Royal College of Nursing and a UK-wide organisation', it clearly demonstrates the success that the RCN is a strong voice for the nursing profession.

Tŷ Maeth as a building engenders huge emotional significance: RCN members in Wales are acutely aware that nurses in Wales raised the funds to secure a building that would place the RCN in Wales at the centre of influence and a place where members could meet to share their views in developing nursing practice and thus enhancing patient care. The fact that nurses embarked on such a journey was both amazing and inspirational and indeed demonstrates that when nurses put their mind to a task, they do achieve outstanding successes.

The RCN in Wales now has two offices: Tŷ Maeth in Cardiff and an office in North Wales. The office in North Wales was originally named Tŷ Tirion and in recent years we moved to a modern office block in Old Colwyn to provide more security and access for our staff and members.

Being a nurse is the best job ever. It is a privilege to care for those in need when they are at their most vulnerable, it is also essential that nurses have the professional help and support when they too are in need.

The RCN is an organisation here for its members, and it is an organisation that is led by its members and we also have an excellent team of staff; and together we are successful.

Best Wishes Tŷ Maeth!

'On the 50th anniversary of Tŷ Maeth, the Royal College of Nursing's Welsh Board headquarters, I am delighted to have the opportunity to thank all the nurses in Wales for your hard work and dedication. I know that your commitment to providing safe, high-quality, compassionate care for the whole community will continue selflessly.'
Rt Hon David Cameron MP, Prime Minister

'Nurses are pivotal in the delivery of high quality, effective care for patients the length and breadth of Wales. It is my pleasure to congratulate the Royal College of Nursing on the 50th anniversary of Tŷ Maeth – in keeping with its name, the building has nurtured the profession over the last five decades. I wish the College all the very best for the next 50 years of developing the profession in Wales.'
David Rees AM, Chair of the National Assembly for Wales' Health and Social Care Committee

'Tŷ Maeth is an incredible testament to the hard work and commitment of the Royal College in Wales and I wish the 'house of nurture' a very happy 50th anniversary. Wales' 24,000 nurses do an extraordinary job, going above and beyond the call of duty every day. It's important that all have a strong voice and I know the RCN – with Tŷ Maeth at its heart – will continue to deliver that.'
Darren Millar AM, Shadow Health Minister

'Happy Birthday to Tŷ Maeth! Here's to the last 50 years serving as the 'House of Nurture' and may we see many, many more years to come!'
Colin Jackson CBE, Olympic Athlete

'I truly value the contribution nursing makes for the people of Wales. I would like to wish a happy anniversary to Tŷ Maeth, the headquarters of the RCN Welsh Board, and to congratulate the RCN on their achievements for the past 50 years in actively supporting and representing nurses and nursing in Wales.'
Rt Hon Carwyn Jones AM, First Minister of Wales

'I would like to congratulate the RCN on the 50th anniversary of their Welsh headquarters. It has been an extraordinary period in Welsh politics with the advent of devolution and throughout the changes the RCN has always been there, standing up for nurses. Here's to the next 50 years.'
Kirsty Williams CBE AM, Leader of the Welsh Liberal Democrats

'Happy Birthday to Tŷ Maeth. The anniversary marks 50 years of the RCN providing strong representation for Welsh nurses and being an unique and powerful advocate for the founding values of our NHS.'
Elin Jones AM, Health Spokesperson

'There is no more fundamental or valuable service than to devote yourself to the care of others in their times of greatest need. It is the most noble of tasks and the highest of aspirations. Our nurses are to be cherished and supported and this building is a physical embodiment of that. A very Happy Birthday to Tŷ Maeth!'
Michael Sheen, Actor and Producer

1959

There are 1,000 members of the Royal College of Nursing working in Wales – all represented from London. Wales is the only country in the UK without its own board. RCN Council agrees in principle to Wales campaigning for its own board, as long as everything is funded from Wales.

1962

Welsh nurses have raised £29,000 for their own Welsh Board. Noreen Thomas is the first chair. Nurses' minds turn to planning for a permanent Welsh headquarters.

1963

Hettie Hopkins becomes Board Secretary.

1978

Anne Pegington becomes RCN Wales's Board Secretary.

1982

RCN Wales now has 13,000 members.

1983

A second floor is added to Tŷ Maeth. HRH Princess Margaret returns to open the Harry Gibson suite, named after a Cardiff businessman who had done much to support Tŷ Maeth.

Timeline

1964

Entertainer Harry Secombe launches an appeal to raise money for a building for RCN Wales. Nurses hold book sales, whist drives, cheese and wine evenings, gymkhanas, and all sorts of events to raise money. They make dozens of appeals to potential donors.

1965

The appeal raises £300,000, double the amount originally hoped for. A location is chosen for the new RCN headquarters. It will be built close to the University Hospital of Wales.

27 October 1965

HRH Princess Margaret officially opens Tŷ Maeth, the new RCN Wales headquarters. She is welcomed by a nursing 'guard of honour' representing all 27 grades and fields of nursing in Wales.

1984

RCN Wales recognises the growing importance of research in nursing. It launches an appeal to raise money to create the first nursing chair in Wales. Chairman Alun Islwyn Giles oversees the group leading the appeal.

1985

An appeal is launched to raise £400,000 to fund the research chair. A number of promises of donations are secured in advance of the launch.

1987

The research appeal hits its target and funds are handed to the Provost of the University of Wales College of Medicine, Herbert Duthie, to set up the first Chair of Nursing Research in the UK.

1959-1987

1988
Dr Judith Maguire becomes Wales's first Chair of Nursing research.

1995
HRH Princess Margaret visits to celebrate the 30th anniversary of Tŷ Maeth.

1997
Board Secretary Anne Pegington receives an OBE in the 1997 New Year's Honours List.

2012
RCN in Wales launches its annual Nurse of the Year Awards. Louise Poley is the first Nurse of the Year winner.

2013
Ruth Owens wins Nurse of the Year.

2014
Kirsty Williams CBE AM formally introduces her Safe Nursing Staffing Levels (Wales) Bill to Assembly Members in the Senedd. RCN Wales has worked closely with Kirsty to campaign for the bill.

Veronica Jarman wins Nurse of the Year.

Timeline

1998

Liz Hewett becomes Board Secretary. During her tenure the role changes title to 'Director'.

2004

Tina Donnelly, Director RCN in Wales.

2005

HRH Princess Anne visits to celebrate the 40th anniversary of Tŷ Maeth.

New Year's Day 2015

Tina Donnelly is made a Commander of the Most Excellent Order of the British Empire (CBE) for services to nursing, the armed forces and trade unionism.

2015

RCN in Wales launches its Time to Care 2016 campaign, a manifesto for the Welsh Assembly elections. Safe staffing is central to the campaign.

Claire Harris wins Nurse of the Year.

Next Steps

RCN in Wales has 25,000 members. It celebrates the opening of a refurbished Tŷ Maeth.

Nursing Staffing Bill clears all stages at the National Assembly for Wales and is passed on for Royal Assent.

1988-2015

Early Years

August 1964. RCN Welsh Board Chairman Mary Jones cutting the first sod before the building of Tŷ Maeth.

RCN Welsh Board, 1969.

Rcn Royal College of Nursing and
National Council of Nurses of the United Kingdom

WELSH BOARD

TY MAETH

KING GEORGE V. DRIVE EAST

C A R D I F F

Opening

OF

THE NEW HEADQUARTERS

BY

HER ROYAL HIGHNESS
PRINCESS MARGARET
COUNTESS OF SNOWDON

ON

WEDNESDAY, 27th OCTOBER, 1965

The event programme from the opening of Tŷ Maeth by
Princess Margaret in October 1965.

Above: Tŷ Maeth, 1965.

Right top: A meeting at the RCN Welsh Board dinner, Park Hotel, Cardiff, 1970.
From left to right: Noreen Thomas OBE, Chairman, RCN Council; Miss C. M. Hall, General Secretary; Pauline Matthews, Chairman, Welsh Board; Hettie Hopkins, Secretary, Welsh Board; Squadron Leader M. Williams MBE, Administrative Officer, Welsh Board.

Right bottom: The rear of Tŷ Maeth in 1965.

The Board Secretaries and Directors

Hettie Hopkins OBE
RCN Welsh Board Secretary 1963-1978

In 1965, on this day and at this time*, I was waving off two engineers and some fitters who had been adjusting the seating for the lecture theatre. It was found when they came to fit these seats the day before that they were three millimetres too wide for the space available on each tier. They worked all night and we were here very early on in the morning. It was a relief to wave them off and we managed to be clean and presentable when Her Royal Highness [Princess Margaret] arrived at three o'clock. That was 40 years ago today.

How did this dream come about? In 1959 there was a Welsh uprising of nurses. [RCN] Council was about to reconstitute itself and, as well as proposing to include men in the charter, they wanted to reduce the three Welsh council members to two. Mary Davies, the distinguished health visitor tutor from the Welsh National School of Medicine, and Eileen Rees, the matron of the Cardiff Royal Infirmary, both council members, were up in arms and soon let the nurses of Wales know what was proposed.

They pressed Council to allow us to keep the three members and to have a full-time officer for Wales instead of three so-called part-timers who occasionally came over the border from the north of England, from mid-England and from the south of England to service the members in Wales.

They were not happy about this but such pressure was put on Council that eventually the president said if you really mean business and you can raise £20,000 within two years you can have a full-time officer who can live at home and use her own car. Well, that was something and an interim committee was formed, led by the two ladies, and representatives from every branch in Wales were appointed to this committee. They set about meeting in various parts of Wales to break down the isolation that had been felt. They each were given a target to reach towards this £20,000. It does not sound much these days but it was a lot of money then.

Individuals and branches and groups of nurses, and many, many husbands, all joined in with these branch efforts. I had several projects. I was a very happy tutor at the Cardiff Royal Infirmary in charge of the preliminary training school and I took my staff nurse, Marion Bull, at five o'clock in the morning, along with a few students, one St David's Day, to the flower market in Cardiff and we bought boxes of daffodils and we returned to the hospital and sold these daffodils for a shilling each to anybody and everybody. Patients loved it and we made a lot of money. That was just one effort; I could tell you many stories, but time does not permit.

The general appeal, the branches effort by the interim committee, raised £20,000 in just over 18 months, and madam president had to admit defeat and express her surprise – indeed she apologised for such lack of faith in the Welsh nurses! A full-time officer was appointed and she had one meagre office in Greyfriars Road in Cardiff and she was in post for a few months. She did a brilliant job while she was in post because she knew contacts, social contacts, all

over Wales and got things going well towards raising more money, because Council had said on no account were we to put a foot outside Wales for any money. We were to be entirely self-supporting, otherwise Council might lose some of its donors. We were strictly bound to raise our own money for the future and this building of course is evidence of that.

In November 1962, the Welsh Board replaced the interim committee and Noreen Thomas, a very distinguished lady from Colwyn Bay hospital, a matron there, who had a very brilliant career, became the first chairman.

An appeal secretary was appointed and that was a very clever move because he had just left post as appeal secretary for the National Museum of Wales. He knew the ropes and he had all the links, and he quickly got into position.

In March 1963, Council sanctioned the formation of a national appeal committee. In May I was appointed secretary to the board. I had had no aspirations towards it at all because I was very happy as an old-fashioned sister tutor. I loved the work, I did not want to leave it. I had lived in hospital for 28 years and I did not like the idea of moving outside. I had had no administrative experience hardly and I had never had a secretary, so I was quite naïve. But Eileen Rees and Mary Davies both said you should apply. I resisted this for ages. They told me that I had a supportive family, I could live at my home, which was near Cardiff, and I could use the family car, which was a Morris 1000. Well, eventually, with such support, I did develop an inner conviction that all should be well and I found myself being interviewed at headquarters.

One of the questions I was asked was: 'Is there any aspect about this job that you think would worry you, Miss Hopkins?'

I said: 'If it's got anything to do with trade unions I shrivel up.'

And she said very loftily: 'I think we can help you in that respect.'

I was happy on the professional side but I needed a lot of help otherwise.

In October 1963, the national appeal committee was appointed under the chairmanship of Sir Godfrey Llewellyn and presidency of Sir Tudor Thomas, and it was composed of many distinguished people from throughout Wales.

Although some unity had been created among the nurses during the interim committee's time, there was a cultural barrier between north and south. In the BBC, and many government organisations, north and south had nothing to do with each other. It was not just a language thing. The country roads made journeys long and arduous. Some days it took me seven hours to drive from home to Bangor in my Morris 1000 along the winding roads. I used to keep myself going with shilling cartons of milk that

were available at the national milk kiosks along the roadside, and biscuits bought from Boots. But whenever I arrived at my hostesses' I would always have a jolly good meal. It was the matrons and the senior people in the profession – the board members – who invited me and fed me and put me up overnight. It never cost the college a penny! There was great generosity.

I concentrated on reaching the people who had felt so isolated from Cardiff. They complained to us that everything happens in Cardiff so I went to the north first of all, all along the north coast, and got to know the people, spoke at branch meetings, walked around hospitals, met district nurses and made good friends with chairmen of board of governors and hospital management committees. Those friendships proved very profitable in the future: we were allowed to do anything in the hospital, college-wise.

I stayed at the homes of nurses, and in matron's flats, and it always meant late night talking and early work next morning. It was great; I loved it.

As I was travelling I would always call in any cottage hospital that I was passing and if I saw a brass plate for a district nurse I would ring the bell or knock the door and if she was in I'd have a chat and a cup of coffee and let her know what was going on... and if she was not a college member she soon became one!

It was wonderful working all along the north. You see I was a mongrel: my mother was a north Walian, my father was a south Walian and I'd lived in both north and south, and my home was then in mid-Wales.

I travelled 17,000 miles in less than 18 months, sometimes accompanied by headquarters staff who enjoyed being driven around the beauty of Wales. I loved meeting the people and selling to them the idea of boosting the professional voice in Wales and developing professional leadership.

The membership doubled very quickly, especially among district nurses and I really found great satisfaction in this work.

I also had hospitality from many of the distinguished national appeal committee members in wonderful homes. One suggested that the college should have an exhibition at the National Eisteddfod every year. We took this up and I spent a week at each venue each year and what began as an appeal venture became a professional service to nurses who visited from all over Wales.

In August 1964, as the excitement mounted and all Wales knew about nurses and the college, we began a very wonderful story. [The appeal raised £200,000 for a Welsh headquarters – Tŷ Maeth.]

The Tŷ Maeth site was chosen, a price was fixed and we were prepared to pay for it from the appeal money. But it was found that there was a sewer going under the building and the price was reduced to about £1,200 and the site was secured. Once we had dug the first sod and gone on with the building it was found in fact there was no sewer at all. So we were very blessed indeed!

As a special dispensation we were allowed to move in to this building three months before it was completed. Can you imagine? Concrete floors, trailing wires and flexes, fittings lying loose everywhere, dirt and dust, no water, telephone or electricity for hours at a time. We were very cold and very dirty but we still kept working towards the big day.

[Tŷ Maeth was officially opened on October 27, 1965.] In September 1965 the appeal committee was disbanded, it had been challenged to raise £200,000 and Wales was well over target – it raised £300,000. The president was very amazed. People wanted to know how we had done it.

Our £300,000 is now worth £4m so we were very proud.

We were very proud, naturally, of this building which was opened by Her Royal Highness Princess Margaret.

Ever so many of the nursing staff had travelled around Wales with me [during the campaign]. Peggy Nuttall, of the Nursing Times, wrote wonderful articles afterwards praising the district nurses in the remote mountainous areas of Wales, the health visitors in the mining valleys and the wonderful staff nurses in the cottage hospitals.

We were very proud, naturally, of this building which was opened by Her Royal Highness Princess Margaret. We had a memorable day.

Taken from a speech made in 2005 on the 40th anniversary of the opening of Tŷ Maeth.

Anne Pegington OBE
RCN Welsh Board Secretary 1978-1998.

RCN Wales had always been important to me. I felt every nurse should belong to a professional organisation. In those days we used to consider the RCN a tripartite organisation: it was a professional organisation, an educational establishment and, from the late 1970s, it became a trade union. That gave members security: they knew that if they were in trouble they had an organisation to turn to.

My predecessor was Miss Hettie Hopkins and she surely was responsible for the foundation of the College in Wales. She also remained with the College for 20 years.

Miss Hopkins had been the driver behind the fundraising campaign. Not only was there adequate funds to build Tŷ Maeth, there was also enough funds to furnish and equip the building.

Princess Margaret opened Tŷ Maeth and she visited again twice during my time. She came to open the extension we had built and she was an absolute delight. She was our patron.

Tŷ Maeth was named by Hettie's father, who was a pastor, and it means the House of Encouragement/Nourishment.

*

I had a team of officers who represented all nurses. I think our strength as a College was we were always available if a nurse needed to talk or was in trouble.

It was difficult for nurses to accept when we became a trade union but, once we trained our nurse stewards and they became readily available, nurses saw the value of the trade union. From the outset we received numerous

I trained in the North Middlesex Hospital in the late 1950s. I came back to Wales almost immediately and was employed by Gwent Health Authority. I stayed there for almost 18 years, mainly in managerial roles.

I was appointed to the position of Board Secretary in 1978.

calls from nurses who were in trouble on the wards and we would represent them, mostly winning their case because of the additional knowledge we had.

Nurses throughout Wales had a branch structure where nurses would meet monthly, giving them the opportunity to voice their opinions. These opinions would then be brought to the Welsh Board.

Above: Anne Pegington, RCN Welsh Board Secretary, and Alun Giles, Chairman of the Welsh Board, with Dame Catherine Hall – Mayoress of Cardiff – who was being presented with a model spinning wheel by Board Member David Jones, of Gwynedd. Date unknown.

Right: Anne Pegington, RCN Welsh Board Secretary, 1978-1998.

RCN Wales reports the visit of Princess Margaret to Cardiff to celebrate
the 30th anniversary of Tŷ Maeth in 1995.

The Welsh Board was made up of representatives from throughout Wales. The two longest chair persons during my term of office were Alun Giles, sadly now deceased, and Meg Edwards.

RCN Wales as an organisation is very well respected.

RCN Wales as an organisation is very well respected. Media attention was always at the forefront. Broadcasters were always very interested in what we had to report. I felt we were quite a power, and a force to be reckoned with. I was proud that Welsh Board was outspoken and, although politicians did not always agree with us, they always listened.

I also think that through our representation we helped make improvements in healthcare. A new method of training came in for student nurses and we, in Wales, were far in advance of England at the time.

I think nurses work hard. I have been a patient over the last few years and I am amazed at the workload. Having said that I would like to see our nurses communicate better, to have more contact with patients, and sometimes there just does not seem the time to do that anymore. Patients feel lonely and, when they see nurses running up and down, they sometimes feel they would like someone to come and have a chat.

People say nursing is a vocation. I agree it is, but you must want to care. Not every youngster wants to do all the menial tasks that one still has to do as a nurse, whether you are at the top or the bottom. I realise that I would be well behind now on training and knowledge, but I could still make a patient comfortable and I think that is important.

The way nurse education training itself has improved, though, is wonderful. The best way I can describe it is that the academic attainments of being a nurse are the same now as any profession: doctor, physio, occupational therapist.

*

During my 20 years we took delegations to the Secretary of State for Wales seven times. If ever we had a serious problem we would approach the Chief Nursing Officer of the day at the Welsh Office, as it was then, and we would be heard. We found William Hague to be the most sympathetic gentlemen with an ear for nursing.

One campaign was about community nurses having difficulty getting to their venues on Christmas Day if the weather was poor. We gathered together examples of how farmers would help with their tractors to drive a nurse who had to give insulin to a patient, etc, etc, and we went to the Welsh Office. Our delegation usually consisted of about six of us, including the Chairman of the Board, and we would put our case to the Chief Nursing Officer.

If we felt we were not getting anywhere we would go to the Secretary of State. That access was fantastic. I know we have MEPs now and the National Assembly, but the very close relationship we had with the Welsh Office was quite significant.

RCN Wales chaired the joint staff consultative council, which was made up of all the trade unions and all the professional organisations, and we met every three or four months to talk about things that pertained to Wales. We were autonomous and I enjoyed the autonomy of Wales. We felt that there were times that we could tell London that this issue did not affect them but it did affect us, and therefore it was for us to deal with. It was important; we saw ourselves as a country in our own right which we are.

All the board secretaries/directors have fought hard to keep that autonomy.

Liz Hewett
Director RCN in Wales 1998-2004.

I qualified as a nurse in 1974 after doing my training at the Middlesex Hospital in London. I spent a lot of my time working in the Accident and Emergency Department, partly at the Middlesex and then later on at the Leicester Royal Infirmary where I spent the best part of 10 years. Gradually as I became promoted I found myself in management roles, mainly within the NHS in Leicester, before moving to Wales, which is where a lot of my more senior management experience was undertaken. That culminated in me joining the RCN Wales staff in 1998.

My role was known as 'board secretary' at first but it later became known as 'director'. It was a very exciting role in many ways; it was the most senior position in the organisation in Wales, and it gave me many opportunities. I obviously had staff to manage and all the resources that were allocated to us, but the central part of the RCN

is its members. That meant that by far the most important role was making sure that members were looked after in employment matters if they required it and, on a higher level, ensuring that nurses and nursing were properly represented at all levels of healthcare. Looking after the best interests of nurses means that ultimately you are looking after the care of their patients.

The RCN is quite a complex organisation in terms of what it is there to do. I see three clear purposes of RCN Wales. It is there to represent its members; it acts as an educator, providing many learning opportunities for its members; and it is a political influencer.

I was lucky enough to be in Wales during a most exciting period as it was when the referendum for devolution took place. That came in as a 'Yes' result so we then had 60 new National Assembly members who were essentially political rookies needing and wanting to be informed, educated and influenced in a positive way about nurses, nursing and healthcare. A lot of our work at that time became about working alongside and with AMs and their civil servants – the Chief Nursing Officer, primarily, and her team of nursing officers as well.

Political campaigning was critical to the way we needed to operate.

The opportunity to positively influence and to get into the minds of AMs made it a fascinating few years. It was a real team effort. At that time, and I am sure it is the same now, RCN

Wales had a great team of staff, which we were able to grow when health became devolved. They were able to get out amongst the National Assembly members and network to influence a wide variety of people.

Political campaigning was critical to the way we needed to operate if we were to be a serious player in the marketplace, representing our members, representing nursing and trying to positively influence the way forward for caring for the wider population of Wales. We led campaigns. We had lots of meetings with AMs, with civil servants, with NHS managers, all aiming to bring to the fore the importance of nurses, to recognise and value nursing, whether it was within the NHS or outside of it, in the care sector, care homes, schools, wherever people needed care.

*

We ran the Value Nursing campaign in 2003. It grew out of a survey that we undertook amongst our members which looked at how nurses were feeling and whether they felt valued or not. It was clear at the time that people felt quite low in their morale in their workplace. There was quite a lot of evidence of bullying and harassment in the workplace. Nurses felt underpaid, undervalued and not really in positions of authority and power that could help them make things better.

We were able to use that data from the survey to create the campaign. Out of it came a lots of meetings with politicians and managers. We got together an all-party National Assembly group, which included AMs, civil servants, NHS managers and us, and that was very positive. One of the AMs at that time had a nursing background so that was very helpful.

We were able to positively influence the wider world of nurses and nursing within the NHS.

*

The RCN in Wales is a great institution which is steeped in history. I was only the third board secretary/director for RCN Wales. The original board secretary, Hettie Hopkins, was the fundraiser to create the building, Tŷ Maeth, and she went around Wales collecting money from miners and all sorts of people to create a fund for the organisation we have now in Wales.

It is a great institution, it is a growing institution and it has evolved enormously over the years that I have personally known it and over recent times under the auspices of the current director.

I would recommend it to anyone who wants to join it, whether they be a registered nurse, a student or a healthcare assistant. Membership ensures that they will be properly represented by one of their own.

The RCN provides lots of opportunities for education. It provides information on standards, in terms of standards of care. It also means that if you are a member you can play that positive part in influencing where your profession goes and that has got to be critical to ensure that at the end of the day those who you are caring for, whether they are in a hospital in a care home, in their own home or in schools, are getting the optimum care from a highly-trained, thinking, professional person.

Being a nurse is a privilege in my view because of the nature of the intimacy in terms of caring for people, both physically and psychologically. I think it is a privilege to be a nurse and I think it provides you with lots of opportunity to undertake different roles, to travel and to work in any number of different places.

But it is important to remember that it is not everybody's cup of tea and not everyone can do it. It is challenging and it is not necessarily valued as highly as we would like it to be, and that has been reflected in the pay scales that nurses receive. Nurses are in a better position now than they have been over the years, but it still has a long way to go to be perfect and we have to keep fighting for the improvement of nurses' lives.

Tina Donnelly CBE TD DL
Director RCN in Wales since 2004.

I have been a member of the Royal College of Nursing (RCN) all my working life and I know how important it is to have a professional body and a trade union that represents nurses and nursing. The Royal College is a UK membership-led organisation which celebrates its centenary in 2016.

One of the reasons that I joined the College was the recognition of the need for nurses to speak up for nurses and nursing. This was also at the forefront of the minds of those who raised the funds to ensure the RCN had a national headquarters in Wales. It is what makes the RCN different from other trade unions in that only a nurse can really speak up for nurses and nursing, and that has been the driving force for

me throughout my career and especially during my time in RCN Wales – a passion to speak up for our own profession. I know the RCN in Wales makes a significant contribution to the work of the Royal College at UK level.

Tŷ Maeth was opened in Cardiff in 1965 in close proximity to one of the largest hospitals in Wales at the time, and this strategic decision was to ensure the RCN's prominence was maintained amongst the Welsh health community.

At that time, there was only a small contingent of RCN members in Wales, but since that time our membership has steadily grown and we now have in excess of 25,000 nurses, midwives and health care support workers in our membership.

The fact that Welsh nurses of the 1960s decided that they wanted an RCN headquarters in Wales and delivered on their vision was an amazing achievement and remains an inspiration to present day members and staff of the Royal College. Since Tŷ Maeth opened in 1965, we have also opened an office in North Wales.

It was immensely humbling for me to review material that was placed in the RCN Welsh Millennium capsule (which is located in an interior wall within Tŷ Maeth in the year 2000). The material puts on record for future generations the immense efforts that nurses in the 1960s made to raise the necessary funds for the building of its headquarters. I was struck by what could be achieved by only three or four dedicated individuals who had a real passion and a combined clear vision of what they wanted for the RCN members in Wales. It is apparent from the historical records of that time, that these passionate nurses really knew how to galvanise their colleagues to achieve the aim of creating an RCN headquarters in Wales. It is clear that they knew how to effectively engage politically and how to engender public support.

Winning the battle to get Tŷ Maeth built was a huge undertaking requiring those involved to put their heads above the parapet to convince RCN colleagues across the UK of the benefits of ensuring that Welsh members had a distinct voice within the RCN. I am not simply referring to a matter of nationality, but to the significance of what it means to be a nurse and to identify within your own community, as knowing your community well fits with what a nursing culture is: that you value the minorities and you celebrate the differences and you care for patients regardless of class or creed.

The fact that the money needed to build Tŷ Maeth was raised by Welsh members themselves, rather than seeking funding from the RCN nationally, has led to a situation whereby members in Wales have a genuine emotional attachment to the building and all that it stands for. This is always at the forefront of my mind when representing the interests of members.

*

In their day-to-day work, the staff of RCN Wales (whether they work in our Employment Relations Team or as part of our Professional Practice Team) meet nurses and other healthcare professionals on a regular basis.

During these meetings, staff have the opportunity to hear about what is happening on the frontline, in both the NHS and the independent care sector. These exchanges demonstrate to us how resilient frontline clinical staff are in what is a very challenging healthcare environment, and how they daily meet the challenges that they face in order to deliver safe, good quality healthcare.

On the whole nursing is in a good place in Wales. There are lots of things we could teach other countries but equally there is so much that we can learn from them too. Although nursing is regulated on a UK basis, healthcare policy and provision is devolved across the UK. This can be challenging. However, the common thread that helps us address this situation is that, regardless of where they live, patients when they are vulnerable need effective, quality nursing care. With this in mind, the RCN across the UK works collectively to promote excellence in nursing practice and to challenge poor practice.

*

The RCN's mission statement is that: 'The RCN represents nurses and nursing, promotes excellence in practice and shapes health policies.'

The most important thing that drives me is a desire to improve patient care and to keep the interests of the patient at the centre of all that we do. When members raise issues with us in confidence, through Frontline First, or in person, we have to listen and take their concerns seriously. We must always remember that things that seem insignificant to us may be important enough to them to the point that it keeps them as individuals awake at night.

When members raise concerns, I believe we have a duty to raise them with health service managers and to seek to resolve them. This can be really challenging; it is probably one of the most testing parts of my role.

Cross Party meeting National Assembly for Wales.

Sometimes, in order to gain a proper understanding of the concerns raised by frontline clinical staff, I go out and work in various clinical environments in order to see at first-hand what those nurses are experiencing and to listen and hear what members are saying. I am only able to do this because I have maintained my registration and my clinical competence. This has always been very important to me, as I believe the fact that I am a practicing nurse enhances my credibility with members and the health service managers that I sometimes have to challenge. For example, this approach was effective recently when

I worked shifts at a hospital in Wales, after members raised concerns. My intervention culminated in a review of the service which has subsequently led to an improved situation.

The fact that the various health boards in Wales work in different ways and approach problems differently can prove difficult. The RCN in Wales overcomes this difficulty by working through local and national partnership arrangements. We have a reputation of being a very effective organisation in partnership working in Wales. This does not indicate a cosy relationship between ourselves and management; rather it indicates management's respect for our professionalism and our ability to exert appropriate challenge.

An important part of our role is to work effectively with the media. If an organisation works with the media appropriately, it will get its message across and this can contribute to effectively addressing members' concerns. It is also important that we challenge politicians and the status quo if our members believe that patient care is being compromised. That's why our members trust us; they know we are doing things to benefit patients and that, in turn, increases our membership numbers and, so, our power to influence.

*

As Director of RCN Wales, I have to balance two perspectives as I fulfil my role. I have to be an effective trade unionist, representing members, whilst at the same time being a compassionate nurse willing to speak out to make things better for nurses and patients. Having the weight of the nursing profession behind me strengthens my ability to challenge the status quo.

As well as offering them protection, the RCN provides its members with a voice. Sometimes frontline nursing can be a very lonely place and the RCN has a very important role to play in supporting members during difficult times.

Visit to Neonatal Unit Royal Gwent Hospital, Newport.

Nine times out of ten nurses enjoy their profession and they enjoy the work they do but there will be times at the end of a shift when they think they cannot take any more. Those are the times nurses are glad they have joined the RCN and are able to make their voice heard.

If people join the RCN they can become an active participant or a passive recipient; nevertheless, collectively, they are part of a sizeable force to be reckoned with.

*

The RCN trade union activists that came to talk to me when I was a student nurse told me the benefits of having a nurse talk about nursing, especially when you need to be represented. Over the years I have seen time and again why that is important.

When a representative is looking at issues such as terms and conditions of employment, or the Agenda for Change pay scales, or is trying to

argue the point of what it means to have safe patient care, then he or she needs to be able to understand these issues from a nursing perspective.

This is particularly important when addressing the issue of safe staffing. It is not just about saying that we have got to have a set number of nurses on a shift; representatives need to be able to understand what those challenges are from a nursing perspective to make sure that care is not compromised. If care is compromised, staff will become demoralised and the nursing profession will suffer.

The RCN as a professional body sets standards and within its membership (currently 430,000) denotes the clinical expertise available to inform our work.

Since devolution, RCN Wales has been a significant player in Welsh politics, as a professional body with influence across all of the political parties as well as with Welsh Government.

We are an organisation which can very easily take frontline nurses to meet the Health Minister or to meet members of the Health Committee. This gives our members an opportunity to speak to politicians on a face-to-face basis, allowing them to tell them what is going on in the NHS in Wales. For instance, when I wanted to get a point across about the Safe Staffing Bill, being able to bring a ward sister from the frontline to talk to members of the Health Committee was incredibly effective. You could hear a pin drop as she was giving a résumé of her day.

The development of the Nurse Staffing legislation in the National Assembly for Wales is an example of how we have been able to draw on the expertise of our membership to help influence politicians. Our mandate comes from our members.

At our annual Congress members from all over the UK put forward resolutions or matters for discussion to an agenda committee. Those are debated at Congress and voted on by representatives from across the UK. Those that are agreed are taken up by the RCN Council, which is our governing body, in order to inform the work agenda and foci which is then incorporated into our annual plans. The RCN Welsh Board, which is responsible for overseeing the governance of the RCN in Wales, bases its work programme on the national agenda and the issues of priority identified at Congress and by RCN Council. The Welsh Board also has responsibility for leading on those aspects of the RCN's agenda that relate to devolved issues in Wales.

Safe staffing is an example of how this works in practice. The issue of unsafe staffing has been a concern of RCN members across the UK for some time and has been discussed and voted on at Congress. This culminated in work being undertaken by Council's Nursing Public Policy Committee. The RCN in Wales began to deliver on the safe nurse staffing agenda in 2013 and this continued to be the number one issue for nurses to campaign across the UK in recent years.

In Wales, the RCN has worked with a leading politician who was extremely supportive of the need for safe staffing. Through our political lobbying work we found that the Liberal Democrats had an interest in the safe staffing issue. Initially, Baroness Jenny Randerson was interested and willing to progress our concerns within her party. Subsequently, we attended a Welsh Liberal Democrats conference, following which Kirsty Williams CBE, Assembly Member and Leader of the Liberal Democrats in Wales, put forward the first steps in raising a Private Member's Bill.

There were challenges during the first debate as to why some politicians felt that this Bill should not go forward. The RCN in Wales analysed the transcripts of these statements and offered evidence to answer every issue that had been raised. We held a cross-party event which coincided with the Winifred Raphael Memorial Lecture in the University of South Wales when Professor Linda Aitken was invited to speak immediately prior to her giving the lecture. This was immensely successful as Professor Aitken had undertaken multi-national research providing convincing evidence that legislation was necessary to secure safe staffing.

The RCN in Wales team included Lisa Turnbull, Policy and Public Affairs Adviser, who was supported by additional outside expertise from Phil Hubbard, Helen Mary Jones and Jonathan Morgan. They coordinated an influencing and public education campaign setting out the merits of this Bill. The outcome of this campaign, with full cross-party support, has cleared all stages of the Bill at the National

Assembly for Wales and will now be passed on for Royal Assent. We again worked with Professor Anne Marie Rafferty, CBE, who also provided the evidence-base for Safe Nurse Staffing research undertaken by her work within the UK. We certainly had the opportunity to work closely with members of the National Assembly and members of the Welsh Government in order to progress nursing issues. On a biennial basis, members of the RCN in Wales meet with elected members of the House of Commons and also members of the House of Lords in Westminster and indeed we work with elected members of the European Parliament where health policy dictates.

*

In 2011, the Royal College of Nursing invited health care support workers to be members.

One of our campaign priorities for this group of members is to gain a substantial training

and development programme that will enable them to fulfil their roles effectively and part of this campaign is also for them to become a regulated professional group in their own right.

*

Being a nurse is the best job ever. It enables individuals to provide high levels of care and compassion to people when they are at their most vulnerable, coupled with the immense job satisfaction and the freedom to work globally practicing as a nurse and for me, personally, I have had opportunities to provide care in foreign fields and in areas of conflict which I would never have been able to do had I not been a nurse.

*

The RCN is an organisation here for its members, and it is an organisation that is led by its members and we also have an excellent team of staff; and together we are successful.

Political Campaigns

Board Secretary Hettie Hopkins and Board Chairman Edward Lyons head a delegation to the Welsh Office as part of the 'Be Fair To Those Who Care' campaign in 1974. Also pictured are Mrs C. Rogers and Miss M. J. Owen.

Ted Rowlands MP, the Under Secretary of State, pauses to talk to nurses outside the Welsh Office.

Nurses on the delegation to the Welsh Office included Miss K. Mullen (left) and Miss M. J. Owen (centre).

RCN Wales members take a campaign to London.

1970s

Above: An RCN Wales stewards' course at Abergele, September 1975.
Standing (left to right): Gladys Lucas, Diane Devine, Pat Edwards, Sylvia Pearce, Marie Bailey, Eunice Vincent, Beryl Williams, Gillian Jones.
Seated (left to right): Charles Walker, Dorothy Roberts, Ann Culey (course organiser), Hettie Hopkins (Board Secretary), Gordon Williams (course tutor), Marion Gould, Douglas Venables.

Left top: Attendees at a stewards' course at Tŷ Maeth in June 1979.

Left bottom: Board Secretary Hettie Hopkins (standing right) with RCN Wales members attending a Stewards' Course in June 1977.

Above: The launch of the 'Where Have All The Nurses Gone?' campaign at Tŷ Maeth in 1970. Rowena Rees, of the University Hospital of Wales, enrols recruits to the cause.

Right: RCN Wales staff at the National Eisteddfod in Bangor, 1971.

RCN Wales and I

Meg Edwards

Former Chairman of the RCN Welsh Board,
RCN Council Member for Wales, Vice-Chairman,
RCN Wales Representative.

I left school when I was 18 and went to Liverpool to do my nurse training. Then in 1964 I came back to Wrexham, which is my hometown, to work in the Maelor Hospital.

In 1966 I went to work in Africa and was there for just over 12 months. A colleague I had gone with had reason to seek advice from the RCN while we were out there – she was not in difficulty but needed to discuss some issues with them – and it was great for her, giving her

support and advice the whole time we were there. Because of that I made a pledge that when we came back I would join the RCN. I came back to the Maelor and I became a member immediately.

This was just about the time when the campaign for a Welsh headquarters, Tŷ Maeth, was starting in Cardiff and across Wales so we were the North Wales element of the campaign. I was quite new to the situation and they introduced all the new staff to get involved. I was a night sister at the time so when I was not working I helped out. I very quickly became interested in what the RCN was all about.

There was a buzz in North Wales about Tŷ Maeth. I really did get a sense of that, even in North Wales. Nurses were saying that they wanted their own building; all 19 branches were doing their own fundraising and sending the funds to Cardiff. They were having cheese and wines and all sorts of events, and also contacting firms to get sponsors on board. There was a great deal of support.

I was comparatively new in the nursing profession (10 years) and I did not fully understand at that stage why the RCN was so important to nurses. It was only really when I became a nurse manager myself, and was having to supervise and look after others, that I realised I did need the support of the RCN.

I also realised that having the Welsh presence and the Welsh Board meant we could fight for ourselves. This was all at the time when nursing was going through major changes, with the old matrons gone and us younger nursing officers coming in. Matrons had been around for years, dominating the hospitals, and now suddenly it was not like that anymore. We needed the back-up of a professional body as we were becoming responsible for other nurses and issues related to nursing practice.

Later, when I came to South Wales in 1974 as the Divisional Nursing Officer in Neath and Port Talbot, we were going through another re-organisation, in which nursing structures and the health service were changing. Around that time RCN Wales was looking for members to go on to the board and I was nominated. I loved being on the board and getting involved in the RCN's activities.

I totally immersed myself in the RCN. There were some very interesting nursing leaders around and I wanted a bit of their dedication and talent to rub off on me.

I totally immersed myself in the RCN. There were some very interesting nursing leaders around and I wanted a bit of their dedication and talent to rub off on me. I was looking to other people to nurture me. It was a great learning curve for me being on the Welsh Board, and assisted me in my early days of being a nurse manager.

I was pleased to be in at the early stages and see RCN Wales emerge. The Board Secretary at the time, Hettie Hopkins, was a tremendous person and we got a lot of strength from her in terms of the way she conducted herself and the

way she inspired us to promote the message about what we needed for the future.

*

After a while I became the Welsh representative on the London RCN Council. There was so much change going on in nursing and I thought I want to be where I can have a say on policy changes. I want to influence. The RCN offered me the opportunity to do that.

When I went to London I got a sense of how important it was to have the RCN in Wales. We had RCN Ireland, RCN Scotland and RCN Wales. We felt that we had an alliance as 'the Celts'. One year at Congress there was a debate on an issue to do with pay. We were concerned about it as we felt that we could be outvoted by England. We all got together, made a stand and we won the day. England could see how passionate we all were about protecting our identity in the different countries – it is important to have that identity, otherwise you could get swallowed up inside a large organisation.

*

We were involved in many campaigns. Pay was pretty abysmal and so a lot of what we were doing was fighting for improved pay for nurses. We would head to London for marches, head to Westminster Hall. Politicians were starting to understand that you had to listen to nurses. They had a voice. You can't ignore them. If you want to try and understand what is going on in the health service you need to talk to people at the coal face. And there is no-one better than nurses and doctors.

We were thinking that we wanted to talk to politicians too. We had something to say, and they need to know it.

When I was RCN Wales Chairman with Anne Pegington as Board Secretary, we would have monthly meetings with whoever was Secretary of State. They would come to us; we did not have to go to them. We would have an agenda which

Above: Meg Edwards leads an RCN Wales delegation to meet Ian Grist, Under-Secretary of State for Wales. Date unknown.

we would want to discuss and they were now listening to nurses. They were anxious to know what the RCN board was all about and we had these opportunities to let them know.

At that stage RCN had become a trade union as well as a professional body and people wanted to know from us why that was necessary. We had to have that trade union element as we were looking to protect pay and conditions and working environments for nurses, so we had to have the strength to fight for them as well as offer the professional arm. It is so important that all nurses have the back-up of a professional arm and a trade union.

At that time, when I was Chairman, we had something like 19 or 20 branches across Wales and I prided myself that I went to everyone, to their meetings and talking to the nurses themselves, and if an opportunity arose to talk to whoever managed the hospital I would take it.

It was important to me to hear what people had to say. We started organising sunrise meetings. I had worked night duty and knew what that was like: you always thought no-one ever knew you were there, apart from the patients. I went to North Wales in the early hours of the morning to meet with staff. We would have a cup of coffee and talk about the issues that affected them on night duty, that really mattered to them. That routine then became a thing across Wales, where we would have these sunrise/sunset meetings.

The big issue during this period was the Nursing Research Chair, which my predecessor Alun Giles instigated. We had to fundraise and get sponsors to get the message out to the profession as to why it was important to have research in nursing. To begin with I had to go back and ask myself that question. I knew that we needed it but people needed explanations because we were asking for funds.

Nursing is just in your blood and, whatever else you do in your life, it is there forever.

We needed to have someone who could concentrate on getting a body of nursing research going back over the years so we could explain to people the fundamentals of nursing. You can train a nurse but there is something in the person as well which is not in everyone. We wanted to be able to communicate on an academic level the value of research in nursing. What they used to say years ago, during my training days, is that we were knowledgeable doers: we had tasks to do and we did them parrot-fashion. It became pretty obvious that as well as being a knowledgeable doer you had to be a thinker and know why you were doing it. That rang a big bell with me and I thought this is absolutely right: I did train like a parrot and I did as I was told. No-one ever told me why I was doing it that way so this is why developments in research and nurse education are so key.

The research work and improvements in nurse education have enhanced nurses' practice because they now know exactly why they are doing what they do. We used to go around with a prescription and very complicated medicines, put them out and give them to the patients. Did I ever understand what these tablets were? No. Now you can't do that. You have got to understand the pharmacy of medicines, why they are being given, so that you can explain to the patients. Not many patients these days will just take a tablet off a spoon without asking what it is and what is it going to do. So the way we train and educate nurses has come a long way in the last 50 years.

I know many excellent nurses who work so hard and have followed their education, and gone on to do further degrees, wanting to pass on their knowledge. We have highly-qualified skilled nurses in Wales who still remain at bedside and want to be at the bedside, and rightly so.

I was lucky to have a career in the most noble of professions. Being a nurse is in your blood. There is no doubt about it. Even though I have been retired 15 years, I can find myself in situations where my nursing instincts still come to the forefront. I am almost looking at people and diagnosing them, thinking that they should go to visit their GP! I never thought when I retired I would still feel like this, but it is still there.

Nursing is just in your blood and, whatever else you do in your life, it is there forever.

*

Over the years Tŷ Maeth has changed physically but the ethos of Tŷ Maeth has not. We are like a family in RCN Wales here and that's how it always felt. When you used to come into the building, you knew all the staff, whereas if you went to London you would be hard placed to find someone twice there that you knew. It is important to us – that family feeling. This building is important to all Welsh nurses, past and present; the whole fabric of the building is important to us.

That passion for the Welsh Board goes back to those stalwart nurses that set us on the road. Any suggestion back then that England might take control was met with a 'Tut tut! No!' I think they would have walked all the way to London if they had needed to, to make their point.

Eirlys Warrington

RCN Welsh Board Chair 1999-2007 and
Former Chair of RCN Council.

Nursing was something that I wanted to do since I was a small child. My eldest sister was a nurse, my mother was a nurse, so it was just something that followed on really. It was a need within me. Being a nurse is the best job in the world.

I started training in 1960 when students were not allowed to join the RCN. My friend and I thought this was not fair so we planned to start a student nurses' association within the hospital we were training in.

We got it all organised and set up and were duly sent for by the matron of the day who said, 'How dare you!' So we put our case and said we did not think it was very fair to us as students as

we needed the protection that the College could give us but we were not allowed it. She did not accept that and told us that if we did not stop she would discontinue our training so we had to stop.

Then the minute I was able to register as a nurse the first thing I did was join the RCN. I cannot describe it. It was like drawing on a huge comfort blanket.

I did my training in the North of England but when I came to Wales in 1970 I read all about the way Welsh nurses had come together to create RCN Wales. I was absolutely amazed and full of admiration for the people who had done it. It must have been a huge struggle. I know that when I was Chair of the Board the chain of office that I wore had on the back that it was donated by the Cadbury family in Birmingham so the nurses raising money must have written all over the place for donations. Everybody got behind the Welsh nurses.

*

I became an RCN steward, taking on industrial-type training to help colleagues who were in trouble. I represented nurses until I retired. I decided to stand as a member of the board for what was then South Gwent and held that role for eight years. From that experience I stood for Chair of the Board because I could see that changes needed to be made, and I was lucky enough to have the membership vote me in.

I then set about making a whole lot of changes within the board which I felt had been quite old-fashioned. We changed the agenda to fit in with Council agenda. We enlarged the table to allow staff to have a say on the board, bringing on qualified nurses who had vast experience and could contribute to the board's decisions in the same way as the elected members could. I was very proud of that.

I always felt you had to think two, or five, years ahead. We became a very forward-thinking board. We did some good work. Our health and social policy group managed to have a huge input into thinking on the health effects of open-cast mining in Wales.

*

I was Chair of the RCN Council twice and on the second occasion I decided I would like to make changes that I thought were perhaps a bit more progressive.

There were only two members from Wales, two from Scotland, two from Northern Ireland and 18 from England so I had to get the confidence of the English voters, as even if I had got Northern Ireland and Scotland behind me I would still need more votes. I was able to do that and so make quite a few changes, particularly in bringing the decision-making back to Council and to broaden and enlighten the debate within Council on behalf of nurses and nursing.

Being on Council gave me a further sense of why it was important to have a Welsh voice.

There were still large elements out there that considered Wales to be a region of England and thought that they could speak best on our behalf. We knew that was not the case. Wales is a country in its own right.

There was a good example of this when they wanted to reduce the numbers on Council. They drew up a white paper for us to read and debate. In the paper it said the RCN in London planned to reduce each region to have just one member from each region sitting on council.

So I read this paper and went into the debate. I was asked, 'What do you think of the paper?'

and I replied: 'It is great as it gives us an extra seat.'

There were shocked faces. 'No,' they said, 'no, it doesn't. It takes one from you.'

I smiled and said: 'No, no, no. Wales is a country in its own right and for the European Parliament we have three regions in Wales, so that gives us three seats.' That white paper never saw the light of day again! That is my knowledge of Wales influencing the debate in England. They tended to think of us as a region but we were not – we are not.

*

RCN Wales represents nurses throughout Wales. Its strength lies in its local knowledge and its local applications, and the fact that it has such a huge input into the health leadership: it speaks to the assembly on behalf of the nurses in Wales and I think it has huge influence.

I did my training in the North of England but when I came to Wales in 1970 I read all about the way Welsh nurses had come together to create RCN Wales. I was absolutely amazed and full of admiration for the people who had done it. It must have been a huge struggle.

Here in Wales there has always been a lot of discussion about the National Assembly and a lot of people still say that it is a talking shop. However, if you have had something to do with the assembly, which I was lucky enough to do, you realise that we now have a huge input into how we can influence nurses and nursing in Wales – influence that we never had before devolution. Until then political influencing was always done in London by the General Secretary of the RCN on our behalf; now we do it for ourselves and we have huge influence in the assembly.

The assembly has always been very open to two-way conversations. I think they are the same with any profession. They listen to the people of Wales. They have to or they will be voted out.

We now have an input directly to the Health Minister for Wales, through Tina and her team. As and when they need to they will take board members to see the politicians.

The board has continued to always look to the future and with Tina at the helm this has been enhanced enormously. Her experience as a civil servant means she has knowledge of the ins and outs of the Welsh Government and politics.

*

RCN Wales is an organisation that is run by nurses for nurses and when you are in trouble a nurse will represent you. That is an important issue for a nurse because not everybody understands the intricacies of nursing, the minutiae of nursing. If you belong to another union it could mean you are represented by someone who worked in another industry away from nursing, who has little or no understanding of nurses, the way nurses work and the trouble that nurses can easily get into. It is important that nurses represent nurses.

Jackie Davies
Ward Manager, RCN in Wales representative and RCN Welsh Board Member.

I was studying for my A-levels and my headmaster was not happy that I was spending too much time in the sixth-form common room and he insisted I do some voluntary work so I toddled off to the local psychiatric hospital every Wednesday. I had never been in any kind of environment like that before but I really loved the patients and the nurses were lovely to me.

I was 17 or 18 and it was a big old-fashioned, scary-looking building but inside there was a lot of warmth. The wards were really friendly, the patients were happy and there was a lot of banter. Even though I was just a volunteer the nurses wanted to show me how things were done and they told me funny stories about their experiences. I had a sort of 'light bulb moment' and thought: 'This is what I am going to do – I am going to be a nurse'.

I started off in what you call acute admission wards in general psychiatry and then I went and specialised in secure psychiatry in the forensic service. That can be a challenging environment but it is rewarding in itself. These are patients who are ostracised by society on two fronts: one they have a mental illness and two they have an offender background.

I can remember my dad telling me I shouldn't want to work with them. He was worried about his little girl and did not understand. Even now, all these years later, he is still a bit concerned.

The majority of patients I have worked with come from disadvantaged backgrounds. Sometimes when you read their story you can see how they have ended up where they are. They have had a lot to contend with in their past. I have seen these people have the opportunity to move on and to live independently in the community and to avoid reverting back onto the road to offending.

I like people, I am a sociable person, and I am one of those people who find caring for other people rewarding. It makes me feel good about myself. I would say that over my 30-year career I have had a lot out of it as well. I have seen a lot of things, done a lot of things, met loads of wonderful people from very diverse backgrounds and every day has been interesting. Nursing has given me opportunities and experiences I otherwise wouldn't have had.

*

In 1995, I became a volunteer rep for RCN Wales, and because I was a ward manager I had the knowledge, skills and background to help when I was supporting somebody as an RCN rep. One of the things I have always said is that

Jackie Davies at the Nurse of the Year Awards 2015.

being an RCN representative has made me a better ward sister. You see things from different perspectives. The last couple of years I have gone on to represent people more or less full-time – to care for the nurses who care.

In my experience, particularly with the period of austerity over the last few years, it has been important to get nurses to look after each other. I think historically nurses have concentrated on caring for their patients and have not stood up for their own protection: if you think about it, when we had an issue about pay, miners used to go on strike for us. So nurses fighting for themselves is something that they just do not do. If someone says they are going to change their pension, or do this or that to their terms and conditions, it goes against the grain for nurses to do anything about it as they are

looking after people, caring for people and are not naturally antagonistic. Nor do they wish to be on a picket line.

I can remember when we had the dispute over pensions, when there were plans to increase the monthly contribution that people were going to pay and change the retirement age. I was a ward sister at the time and the number of nurses who came to my office, knowing I was a rep for the RCN, saying, 'I can't leave the ward, Jackie... If we vote and have to go on strike, I can't leave the ward that day. What if I am rostered that day? Can you give me annual leave that day because I can't leave the ward?' It caused them real anxiety.

Our work is about trying to get nurses to look after themselves, be activists in terms of promoting their profession but in a way which does not make them feel like they are abandoning the people they are there to care for.

I believe nurses need to be a little bit stronger in terms of sticking up for themselves. There are many little things that nurses are not doing to help themselves: perhaps they are not putting in an incident form that they should have had four nurses on a shift but only had three; they are not capturing the evidence which shows the pressure they are under.

The NHS is run on good will. Nurses are very caring people. They won't leave a shift dead on the dot if there are things that are left to do and they don't claim any additional time owing, so there are hours and hours of their time that they are giving to the NHS.

RCN Wales is part of the solution to that. We can help them by perhaps producing a form that makes it easier for them to capture when they have worked additional hours and sometimes nurses are surprised by how much extra time they are owed in a month. We encourage them to put in incident forms if there has been an incident where otherwise it would perhaps be taken as par for the course. We make them aware of proposals for the seven-day working which is coming in now and discuss how it is going to be funded and how that may affect nurses. We try to get the message to them early so they have knowledge and can react, if necessary.

As a staff side representative, with a nursing background, I have a better understanding of the day to day problems and challenges faced by nurses. I understand the practice issues that they might be having a problem with, as opposed to someone who doesn't have any clinical knowledge or experience. Other trade unions can only focus on processes and policies.

RCN Wales really is a nursing family. We are just nurses. How members deliver direct care

to patients, working in the front line of the NHS. We understand nurses and what nurses need. All our facilities are geared up to the specific needs of nurses, whether it is an employment issue in the workplace or a professional development issue or a learning need. We specialise in nursing.

The RCN's nursing courses teach you things which focus on nursing but also teach you other skills for life. I was lucky enough to go a political leadership course run by the RCN which taught us how to access politicians and how to lobby on an issue you have an interest in but the underpinning theme was promoting nursing, the NHS, and caring for nurses.

The RCN is the true voice of nursing. This makes our contact with politicians so important. I come at it both as a nurse and as an RCN rep. In the last general election I supplied all my friends and family with the email addresses of all the local candidates and the link for the safe staffing bill and said, 'Email and ask your potential MPs what they intend to do?', and they all did that. We also provided statistics to those potential candidates showing how many nurses – and therefore potential voters – existed within their constituency and how important it was to think about the NHS. Then, there is the RCN as a wider organisation, where we actually go as a group of RCN members to the Welsh Government to lobby on issues like safe staffing and other changes to the NHS.

Being a nurse is being part of a family.

Being a nurse is being part of a family, a caring family which allows me to care for others but cares for me too. RCN Wales is the nursing body in Wales which supports, promotes and safeguards the interests of nursing in Wales. The RCN fights for nursing.

Richard Jones MBE
Deputy Director RCN in Wales 1998-2010.

I started my nurse training in 1970. When I qualified my specialty was trauma and orthopaedics and facial maxillary nursing, where I worked as a staff nurse and charge nurse. I then went into what was called a 'nursing officer' role, which was a middle manager in the NHS, and later I went into nurse education, so prior to joining the RCN I was a registered nurse teacher.

Nurse education is the preparation of a registered nurse so that they can skilfully care for patients in any health-care setting. The appropriate preparation of a nurse is fundamental to the delivery of quality care. That was something that was not always a traditional part of nursing development. I was brought up in the apprenticeship scheme, where we went in and out of school, and where the main focus was practical delivery of patient care by a student nurse. Then subsequently nurse education went into universities and in

fact Wales was the first part of the UK in which nursing became a graduate profession. Nurses still had to do the same number of hours in practice as they did previously, but it was much more focused on their educational objectives.

That was a huge step forward. All our colleagues in other professions in the NHS had become graduate professions. So, for me, what was very important was that you had knowledgeable doers – you had nurses who knew what they were doing and why they are doing it. For me that is fundamental in delivering the best possible care for patients.

RCN Wales was the first organisation which actually raised money for a Professor in Nursing Research in the whole of the UK. The professor was based across the road from Tŷ Maeth in the University Hospital of Wales and that role has become fundamental in establishing a body of knowledge for nursing research. The only way to have that good body of knowledge is having researchers doing that work as part of their role. Lots of the nurse researchers would not do it in the university setting – they would do field work out in practice – but that is following the example set by having a Chair in Nursing Research. Research improves the quality of care patients receive and ensures they receive it in the right setting as well.

*

When I first started as a student nurse, the RCN was not accepting male student nurses. But then that changed very quickly and I became a member as soon as men were allowed to join. I felt secure as an RCN member: I knew I had the support of a professional organisation behind me while I was working to deliver care for patients.

I became an activist when I was a tutor. I became a Welsh Board member for Merthyr and Cynon Valley branch and then Vice Chair of the Welsh Board. Towards the end of the 1980s I became much more active in the RCN. Subsequently in 1990 I was fortunate enough to become a professional officer, and then the Deputy Director and Head of Employment Relations until I retired in 2010. As Deputy Director I was responsible for employment relations across Wales so it was a wide remit, but so rewarding.

RCN Wales drew me in across my working life. There were two things that made me very committed to it. The first was a central theme of raising standards of care for patients. Secondly, I felt very strongly about salaries in the nursing profession. I was there to ensure they had a fair deal and that their terms and conditions of service were appropriate to encourage more people into the profession. Our nurses in Wales are very industrious and very professional.

*

I think that alongside giving support to individual members, RCN Wales's work to have political influence is extremely important. We have to put the building blocks in place to ensure they have got a good working environment and ensure there are sufficient numbers of appropriately qualified nurses and healthcare support workers to deliver care for patients whether they are in hospitals, communities, or nursing homes. RCN Wales is there to lobby the government to ensure the Welsh NHS has the right numbers to deliver care.

During my tenure we were initially looking to the government in London. We did not have a Health Minister in Wales; we had a Secretary of State for Health in London and our link to them was the Secretary of State for Wales. So I remember going with Anne Pegington OBE the Board Secretary, as a delegation to lobby the Secretary of State for Wales on the issues of the day.

Then we had devolution and the importance of RCN Wales lobbying on behalf of nurses in Wales became even more essential. Over a third of the budget of the Welsh Government is now spent on health. This makes nursing highly political and with that comes influence, and influencing change is so important. It can only be done by producing evidence for change. Throughout my time working with the Board Secretary and then the subsequent Director of the RCN we would lobby government departments on lots of different issues that would affect nursing across Wales and across the UK.

I have always said that people need to belong to trade unions. There is absolutely no doubt about that. Being a nurse, being a member of the RCN, you belong to just not a trade union but a professional body so therefore you are actually dealing with the up-to-date best practice alongside the best support you can get in your role as a nurse.

As a member of the RCN you are represented by people who have undertaken your job. They know what job you do and they understand the background to your job. RCN reps are coming from a position of knowledge and that is important when they negotiate with employers or governments. They understand nursing and the health service in Wales.

*

Being a nurse is an honour. When a patient discloses things that they would not tell their nearest and dearest you feel so proud that they actually trust you. When you can make a difference or you can give someone a peaceful death by what you do for that patient I think that is such an honour.

As a member of the RCN you are represented by people who have undertaken your job. They know what job you do and they understand the background to your job. RCN reps are coming from a position of knowledge and that is important when they negotiate with employers or governments. They understand nursing and the health service in Wales.

I think the nurses in Wales are very proud of the money that was raised to establish the RCN Welsh Board and Tŷ Maeth. The people in Wales are very generous and because of that we have a building which belongs to the nurses and belongs to nursing in Wales. It is the headquarters of the RCN in Wales and politicians know it.

The government in Wales wants to know what Welsh nurses think; all of the political parties do. I am proud that we don't subscribe to any political party so therefore whatever we are asking for we are asking across the board. We don't favour one party against the other. We are here for patients, we are here for nurses.

Professor Donna Mead OBE FRCN OStJ

RCN Welsh Board Member. Vice-Chair of Cwm Taf University Health Board.

I was born with a congenital orthopaedic condition and I spent many years of my early life in hospitals where I found myself very much admiring what the nurses did. I also found that at primary school I very much admired what the teachers did as well, so I was absolutely torn about what to do: nursing or teaching.

When I was 17 and got my O-levels, I announced that I wanted to be a nurse and the teachers washed their hands of me. They said that would be a waste of a good education and I really felt that they began to dismiss me.

I wanted to prove them wrong so I left school and went to become a pre-nursing student. I became a nurse and, to close the loop on that story, I eventually trained as a teacher as well.

I have been a member of RCN Wales since February 1974, and I was immediately aware of the protection that being a member would give me and of the resources that were available.

I was active from the outset, taking a variety of roles over the years, mainly in the professional side than the trade union side. For example, I became a member of the Research Advisory Group (steering group) in the very early 1980s and took on responsibility for membership, increasing the membership by several thousand while I held that post. Membership is important. For each thousand members you get a seat with voting rights at Congress. I was determined to increase the membership to a thousand to enable the Research Advisory Group to have its first seat at Congress. I was the very proud occupier of that seat and being Welsh added to the sense of pride.

At the time there was an anti-intellectual bias towards research among nurses and research was underrepresented, so I presented the first ever debate in Congress for the Research Advisory Group (now the Research Society) on research. Following this we brought the

Research Society conference to Wales where I was again very proud to deliver a key note speech. I have been a member of the education forum and in doing that I have worked on various task forces to develop education strategies for the RCN. I have given papers at more RCN conferences than I can remember.

RCN Wales work to promote nursing research has been fundamental to improving healthcare. I was fortunate to study for my PhD under the first ever Welsh Board Professor of Nursing Research. Without research, we cannot be certain that what we are doing is the best for patients.

When I was a student nurse the way in which pressure sores were managed was the only thing which gave respectability to witchcraft! It would depend on which ward you went to. One ward would say you turn the patient every two hours if they were bed-bound and you would blow oxygen over the sacral area; the next ward sister would say, 'We don't do that here, we paint the area with egg white or put on talcum powder or something else.'

Then a nurse called Doreen Norton carried out research and discovered the variable which mattered was relieving the pressure by turning the patient. You could put on any potion you liked and it would have no effect whatsoever; only the turning of patients mattered. If ever we needed to be shown the need for research, this study did it.

Historically, nursing has had a huge struggle over research because quite often the kind of research nurses wanted to do, about patient experience, for example, was not the kind which was valued by the medical staff, and certainly not by research councils. That made it very difficult to get funding for that kind of research.

The medical model is diagnose-treat-cure and that lent itself to a research design which is called a trial or a randomised control trial; nurses are often more interested in a treatment's effect on the patient's life and recovery. It has been a long hard struggle to interest the medical community, but it has come to realise that the kind of research nurses do is of interest to them as well.

*

One of the most exciting things that I have done began in 2005 when I was asked on Nurses' Day to do a seminar for RCN Wales in which I could talk about what I liked. I chose to discuss Betsi Cadwaladr, a famous Welsh nurse.

You cannot learn about Betsi without learning about Florence Nightingale. They were contemporaries and they clashed over their methods while treating wounded soldiers during the Crimean War.

I did as much as I could to précis her life and her contribution to nursing, and, at the end of that seminar, I challenged RCN Wales to adopt Betsi as a Welsh nursing icon. That proposal went to the following board meeting and they approved it. In the last 10 years so much has happened which has raised the profile of that individual which has also served to raise the profile of nursing more generally.

You cannot learn about Betsi without learning about Florence Nightingale. They were contemporaries and they clashed over their methods while treating wounded soldiers during the Crimean War.

I do not want to underestimate the achievements of Florence Nightingale, as she brought her political influence and power to bear while trying to raise nursing as a profession, but she did what she did while sticking within the rules. She used statistics, she invented the pie chart and would use bar charts. She was a founding member of the Royal Statistical Society. She would show the politicians what was happening to the soldiers who were injured using statistics. She was the first public health person, I suppose.

Betsi did something very different. She used stories about her patients to go and persuade whoever needed persuading that they needed to give her the tools for the job. She used her stories with devastating effect. If you were an officer in the Crimea and you were injured, you had to pay for your hospital food and for your care. Betsi felt that this was inequitable: She told stories about injured officers who were going hungry because they did not have money on them to pay. Nightingale was unhappy about this as it went against the rules.

Betsi thwarted this rule. Overturned it. Free care, at the point of delivery, regardless of ability to pay but based on need would later become one of the founding principles of the NHS.

Betsi tackled bureaucracy relentlessly. This involved everything from obtaining dressings for a maggot-infested wound to using arrowroot in cooking. Betsi again presented patients' stories to the authorities and used them to mobilise resources until in the end she was not required to have prescriptions. She had open access to the warehouses and she could have what she needed for the care of her patients.

Nightingale and Betsi were both effective. Betsi redesigned complete services and redesigned bureaucracies, and did it all through the medium of telling stories about suffering. But she had been largely forgotten. This was largely due to Nightingale's dislike of 'paid' nurses. She felt that nursing should be delivered by women of good breeding who did not require payment. To be fair, it was the time of the Sairey Gamp, gin-swilling disreputable paid nurses. Betsi was from a new breed of

professional, paid nurses who had undergone training. Nightingale destroyed the records of their achievements.

Getting Betsi recognised for what she had done would have been very difficult as an individual. RCN Wales gave me (1) a platform to speak and (2) a platform for fundraising, and public relations.

Once the RCN Welsh Board had decided to accept the challenge the whole infrastructure of RCN Wales came in behind the campaign for Betsi. Then very quickly the Chief Nursing Officer for Wales decided to endow a Betsi Cadwaladr scholarship in Wales, which the RCN has administered. A Biennial RCN Betsi Cadwaladr lecture was established.

We were very lucky that Tina Donnelly, the Director of RCN Wales, was also an officer in 203 Field Hospital at the time. Through her influence we were able to persuade the Ministry of Defence to name the Welsh field hospital, Elizabeth Cadwaladr House.

Once these things started to happen they had a knock-on effect: hence, the naming of the Betsi Cadwaladr University Health Board. There was opposition to that and it was helpful to have RCN Wales to lead that campaign. There were some who felt Betsi was 'not worthy' of having a health board named after her, so I did the research that demonstrated that many things which had been said about her were nonsense. It was the RCN machinery which ensured that research got to be seen by ministers.

*

As a small country within the UK, it was often the case that the needs of the people of Wales were overlooked. We are similar to regions of England in size but Wales has very specific cultural, health care and economic needs.

I have been involved with RCN Welsh Board at Tŷ Maeth for 42 out of its 50 years existence. The RCN Welsh Board has since its inception

RCN Wales has been responsible for campaigning on so many issues since devolution, sometimes on issues that are not relevant in England and sometimes on issues that would have never have been considered in England because of the scale and the scope.

*

Shortly after devolution I was working in the university sector where my responsibility was to train nurses, midwives and other health professionals.

We had a system among the health organisations in Wales for trying to work out what their workforce needs were going to be in the coming two or three years and that then translated into the numbers that needed to be trained. Effectively, a contracting organisation would inform the universities how many students they needed us to train to provide the future nursing workforce.

This system was not fit for purpose. University applicants apply a year before their course begins. There is competition among universities across the UK to attract the best students. Universities in other parts of the UK were given their numbers early in the academic cycle. In Wales it was often late in the spring before universities received their number of contracted places and by then many applicants had accepted places in universities who were able to provide an offer by the previous December. The Welsh system left us unable to do that as we did not know what numbers would be required. It was very difficult for universities to predict the numbers and make offers because we had been experiencing wide swings in the number of commissions with high numbers one year and low numbers the next. Universities had to be very cautious because once a place (conditional upon achieving qualifications) has been offered and accepted and if subsequently the applicant is successful

(with a home in Cardiff and later in other parts of Wales) been able to make sure that there was a Welsh voice, not just for the sake of it, but because of the issues facing Welsh nurses and their patients. There were different socio and economic issues in Wales and there needed to be a voice to take those concerns to the Welsh Office and later to the Welsh Assembly.

When devolution came it almost seemed as if RCN Welsh Board had always been gearing up for devolved healthcare. The Welsh nursing voice was already here.

In the post-devolution era having an RCN Welsh Board has proved to be absolutely crucial, absolutely fundamental. Across the UK we now have health policies in four countries which are becoming increasingly divergent, but at the centre there is still quite an Anglo-centric view of the world from London.

That means we have to be strong in Wales, to have influence on our own country. Welsh nurses have to be represented in terms of the needs of their patients and the needs of staff by an organisation that has the credentials to talk to Welsh Assembly members.

in obtaining the qualifications, the offer has the status of a legally-binding contract.

As we could not make an offer when the student needed it we were losing great students to the best universities in England which was not best for Wales.

The RCN helped us to get the system changed. It is an organisation that can work with government and deal with issues like that. It was a big step forward as new students are our lifeblood; they are the flow of new staff into the NHS. That change happened very soon after devolution due to the mutual respect the Welsh Government and the RCN have for each other.

*

RCN Wales's most recent campaign has been on safe staffing. I do not know what the eventual outcome of the campaign will be but I do know that this issue is going to be addressed. It may or may not be addressed through a new law- if it did that would be wonderful – but it will be addressed: issues of safe staffing will be a requirement for all health boards.

Whatever happens no more can health boards preside over a situation where nursing numbers decline in order to balance the books and then patient care suffers.

We can never go back to that place as a consequence of the RCN campaign.

*

I have been an RCN member for more than 40 years. A few years ago, I was made a fellow of the RCN and I decided I wanted to be even more active. One of the things I decided to do was to stand for election to the Welsh Board.

My manifesto centred on the balance between the absolutely essential trade union activities and the professional development side of nursing. I felt there needed to be a recalibration of that and so I will see what I can achieve now that I am on the board.

Employment relations matters are obviously very pressing and very time consuming because they are to do with pay and rations, which is extremely important, but I would like more on the professional side of nursing – perhaps we could have a mechanism which provides support to members working in education or research or particular aspects of clinical care such as A&E. Staff develop expertise in these areas and want to network with their colleagues, and I would like to see more of that as part of the RCN's work to promote the art and science of nursing.

*

RCN Wales is effective. It is high profile – as high profile if not higher than many other professional organisations.

RCN Wales is effective. It is high profile – as high profile if not higher than many other professional organisations. It works very closely when it needs to with other professional organisation like the BMA.

It has never taken its eye off the 'patient care' ball and whenever there is the need to mount a campaign on patient care RCN Wales will be there.

It is all Wales. We have a director who has a very high profile, who is very well-respected in both government and health circles.

It works for all levels: students, registered nurses, the service and universities. It is right throughout the profession.

And it delivers. Whether it is fighting and mounting a campaign, or looking after an individual who is facing an employment relations matter, RCN Wales delivers.

Christine Thomas

RCN Convenor and former RCN Welsh Board
Member and former Council Member for Wales.

RCN Wales stands for professionalism. Professionalism in the standards that we have, in the quality of the representation that we give for members and for nurses; the work we do in enhancing nursing. At the end of the day we are all there for the same reason: to ensure the patients have a better outcome. I am really fortunate that I can be part of that.

I became a nurse quite late on. It was not always something I wanted to be. But then my dad died. He had had cancer and I had been looking after him. When I went back to work I just did not feel fulfilled. I thought, 'What am I doing working in a factory when there was so much more I could do?'

Nurse means nurturing and being the girl amongst four boys, and my mum was ill quite a lot, I had always taken on the role of looking after everybody. And I think that's how a nurse starts and that's what makes you want to be a nurse. Then you have to gain all the skills and the knowledge that goes with it. I thought if you were kind you would be fine; of course it takes a lot more than kindness, doesn't it?

I decided to train to be a nurse. At that time I had two boys and I found it difficult, a real struggle in fact. I had left school at 15 with no formal qualifications.

The first week I started my training my mother was taken into one hospital and my husband had fallen and he had to have a laminectomy so he was in a different hospital, and then my brother was admitted to another hospital with TB. That was all at the beginning of my training. So of course I thought, 'I can't do this, I am going to have to pack it up or put it off'. But my tutors were excellent, they understood what was going on and they encouraged me and told me that if I was to go now I would never come back, and they were absolutely right. It was the best thing I ever did.

I qualified then as a nurse and I worked on a medical ward for a while. But my heart was always in the community and so eventually after two years I was successful at gaining a community nursing post. I absolutely loved it, and I did 25 years there.

Around about that time I became involved with the RCN. I started training as a steward in 2001 and was initially a voluntary steward.

The 'Agenda for Change' came about and it was an opportunity for RCN stewards to go into paid hours. It was something we had never had in our organisation. Following on from the introduction of Agenda for Change, I became more involved in the steward role and was actually instrumental in establishing those paid hours. It has developed from there and I have been doing it ever since.

Being a steward gives you immense skills. It gives you negotiating skills and knowledge of HR and employment relations issues. I need all this when I am representing people. The work is very diverse: one minute I am doing a sickness review, the next I am doing a disciplinary investigation or a grievance or a dignity at work.

RCN Wales has given me all these skills. The RCN has opened a lot of doors for me and I have had the opportunity to do things I never ever imagined I would do.

When I first became an RCN council member I was elected as Chair, as my colleague Gaynor Jones is now. That opened doors because one of my first 'gigs', as I like to call it, was actually speaking in Westminster. I could not believe it. I stood looking up at the buildings and thought, 'I can't believe I am here and I have just done this'.

And that sort of experience has just continued. I am very fortunate in that I was chosen to go to Buckingham Palace too. I would never have had that opportunity if it was not for the RCN. I feel very fortunate. I have had a fantastic career as a nurse. I have had a fantastic career as a rep as well.

I think RCN Wales has been very successful at lobbying government and we have the ear of the health minister and have had a connection with previous successive health ministers as well.

We have influence, certainly on the health boards. I am in a partnership forum. One month I chair it, the next month the director chairs it. I can knock on the door of the chief executive and I can speak to him. The health board leaders value the RCN. They know if I am coming from RCN Wales I am taking a professional view. It is a moderated and measured view. I don't march in and say, 'You have got to give this and you have got to give that'. We talk, we negotiate, we find the best ways. When RCN Wales makes a statement it is quite clear about its facts and its research.

Obviously the better the staff feel then the better the patients are going to feel.

We talk, we negotiate, we find the best ways. When RCN Wales makes a statement it is quite clear about its facts and its research.

Being a nurse is like an emotional rollercoaster. The gains are so fantastic. But there are a lot of hard difficult times as well. We sometimes lose patients that we were very, very fond of. Then you have to try to look at it in perspective. It was a privilege to be able make the end of life for that patient as best as it possibly could be. We can't save everybody but we can make their pathway – their experience – a lot better.

Nursing is hard, but I still think it is the best profession in the world.

Jane Carroll
Former RCN Welsh Board Member.

My mum is a nurse, my aunty was a nurse and my grandmother was a nurse, and they discouraged me in many ways not to go into nursing. But from a very young age I knew I would. My earliest recollection was asking my dad to make me beds for my birthday, little wooden beds. I must have been eight or nine. We had mattresses made for them and sheets and I had three of them in a row. I ran a nursing ward, at the age of nine. It was a given that was where I was going.

My aunty would sometimes look after me in the summer because my mum worked and I would go up and stay with her and my grandmother. She would take me on to the ward. I loved going on there. I like talking to people anyway and I really enjoyed that interaction; from there it was like a natural progression.

I am not one of those nurses who may say, 'Oh, don't go into nursing!' To me it is a fabulous job. There is so much variety to what you can do, to the areas you can specialise in. At no stage have I ever imagined myself working in anything other than a nursing role.

More than 20 years ago I had a colleague who really started to make my life very difficult. I am quite an outspoken person, I am quite transparent, and this particular individual started on me. I got in touch with a local representative, Eirlys Warrington, my mum, who represented me and helped me put in a complaint. After that representation I realised that I wanted to be a steward. I wanted to have the same impact for other people that she had for me.

I love the activism. Since becoming a steward I have always been involved in my branch. I love the camaraderie that a branch offers you. You can bring those nursing issues in and talk about them, share them with others. I am proud in being a steward because I feel I can speak up about issues that others might be nervous to raise and I can represent them.

The role offers you a voice as well – particularly in Wales where we have a close working relationship with the Welsh government. We have easy access to our ministers and if you have a particular concern you can take it straight to the minister.

I think being part of RCN Wales gives you instant credibility among many groups of quite powerful people who want to hear what you have to say as a nurse. We are not only a trade union, we are a professional body. We are the Royal College of Nursing and I think that is what has the kick that says to people we have got a little bit more behind us.

There is a responsibility that comes with that as well. I think that can be quite onerous because you have to ensure that what you are saying is accurate and that you are representing your members honestly – that you are speaking their view, not your view. Being a steward teaches you a lot of skills which I would not have had if I had not been active in the RCN.

I am proud in being a steward because I feel I can speak up about issues that others might be nervous to raise and I can represent them.

While I don't work in a hospital, I have good networks now within the hospital so that I can go and meet with members and they can feed back to me the information about what is happening in their area. I can feel reassured that that evidence is accurate so it is important that you develop those networks around you, networks that people want to be a part of and in which they engage with you and the wider nursing family through the RCN.

I have spoken at several events in Welsh Government, have met with ministers around particular health issues, and been on the political leadership course which the RCN Wales runs, and that has helped me an awful lot. It means I know how to gauge conversations and to get my point across accurately and fairly quickly. It has helped me to know what I need to say at the meetings.

Politicians do listen to RCN Wales and they want to hear what we – as RCN Wales representatives – have got to say. They want to engage with us because they know that we have something valuable to share with them. They know that because of our background in nursing that our point is not necessarily a political one and that it is about keeping nurses and patients the focus of what we want to say.

The big issue at the moment is safe staffing. We have a shortage of nurses. Safe staffing is hugely important for every nurse, and not only those in a hospital environment. I work in the community and it is important for us too that we have adequate numbers of nurses to care for an increasingly older population who deserve good nursing care.

*

I always say it is worth being a member of a trade union as it offers people protection if they are in trouble at work, but what the RCN offers in addition is professional support on top of employment support.

Members have access to a phone line straight away if they are in trouble, they do not have to wait to speak to someone. They have access to a large library. If I am on a course I will always phone up the RCN library because the librarians will undertake a relevant literature search for you. I have borrowed books off them because very often if you are on a course at a university the books that you need in their library go quickly. If you are a member you don't necessarily have to use that university library, you can use the RCN one. The librarians are great. You phone them up and if you have got a query they will look it up and get back to you very quickly. As I work full-time it saves me an awful lot of time.

I had an issue where a member contacted me about driving a bus with learning disability patients in it. I was not sure what the rules were around that. I contacted the library and the librarian searched up any relevant health and safety guidance for me and any relevant policies that may be out there from other areas. That supported us then in that conversation with their manager about that.

I think Tŷ Maeth is important to members across Wales because it gives them a sense of having a place in Wales. Rather than Cavendish Square being the centre point, for the last 50 years we have had this headquarters which we can call ours. We can hold meetings here, have a visible presence here and that is why it is important. Plus nurses feel close to the historical background of Tŷ Maeth, to the fundraising that built this place. Welsh nurses raised the funds to build it. I think that sends a huge historical message to our members.

That sense of ownership is something we should never lose. I view this building as a symbol of Welsh nurses, past, present and future.

Jane Carroll, David Williams, Vice Chair of the RCN Welsh Board, William Graham AM and Richard Jones MBE.

Wayne Parsons

Senior Nurse, Winner, Innovation in Nursing Award, RCN in Wales Nurse of the Year 2014.

For me, nursing turned out to be a vocation. I can't really say why. I was in a totally different career at the time but I decided to switch and from day one I knew nursing was for me. Today I remain totally obsessed and passionate about nursing.

As an A&E nurse I like it best when the work is busiest and hardest; when we are in a crisis situation, is when we enjoy the job the most.

It is the adrenaline; it's the satisfaction you get out of seeing a sick patient become well. It's really about the patient and the patient outcome, and that is why I find it so satisfying.

I believe people have to really want to be a nurse. If that is what they want I would encourage them to go for it. I think it is very much a vocation.

We worked very hard to become a professional body and to create degree nurses, but people have to come into it for the right reason. I think

as long as that person has an understanding of what the job entails and they have shown that sort of thinking and ethos before they go into it, then that can only be good for the profession.

You need to feel it. You need to care otherwise you are going to struggle to get up in the mornings and come into work because it is stressful. It is a difficult environment to come in to. You are put under pressures and there are many demands, but I think if you keep the patient at the centre of what you are doing each day then that's what gives you the drive to keep coming back.

Nursing is something that you need to see as a vocation and nurses need to feel passionately that they can make a difference in someone's life.

From my point of view, being a nurse is exciting and exhilarating; it is certainly challenging but I wouldn't want to do anything else.

Tamara Morgan
Staff Nurse, RCN Welsh Board Member.

I became a nurse by accident really. I started working in a nursing home when my children were young. I quite liked being a nursing assistant and I thought I could do this. So I tripped off to university and to start off with I was going to be a mental health nurse. Then I got a job in A&E as a nursing assistant and I really liked making a difference.

Being a nurse is an honour. It is without a doubt one of the most demanding things you can do but it is also the most rewarding. I would not change it for the world.

In ICU you get to see patients on the worst days of their lives, when they receive the worst news possible for them. But we also get to give them the good news: we are there when they wake up; we are there when they go to sleep. We can hold their hand and can say that we have 100% done our best.

Knowing you have put in that commitment is worth every bad day, it is worth every late shift, every late return home and the three hours you stay on... When a patient speaks for the very first time after not being awake for several weeks on end and their words are, 'Thank you', it means the world. You cannot buy that, you really can't.

I took up my seat on the RCN Wales board at the end of December 2014 and prior to that I was a student board member. As a student I was kind of swept under its wing and taken to RCN Congress.

RCN Wales is massively important, not only as a trade union but also as a professional body. It gives members support from a legal and professional aspect, and gives them great training.

My membership of RCN Wales has given me so many opportunities within nursing. I have attended training days which I would not have had the opportunity to do otherwise. It organises the Nurse Leadership Summit and the Nurse of the Year Awards which are really important to nurses and nursing.

RCN support is there 24 hours a day. It has information online for the hours when offices are shut. Many times I have opened up the computer at 2am while in work to look up something that I did not know. We regularly refer to the RCN's training regimes in work.

Tina Donnelly, our Director, and Gaynor Jones, our Chair of Welsh Board, are two of the most inspirational people you will ever meet. Knowing that I can phone up any member of staff from RCN Wales or HQ in London

'Two of the most inspirational people you will ever meet': RCN Wales Director Tina Donnelly (left) and Board Chair Gaynor Jones (right) with David Rees AM, Chair of the Health and Social Services Committee, at the launch of the *Time To Care* 2016 campaign.

for advice makes a tremendous difference. Someone is there on the end of a phone to listen, to know what my problem or my concern is.

RCN Wales really does recognise nurses for being nurses, and I think that is really important, especially in this climate.

Student nurses are really looked after. The RCN has a student committee which has members from across the UK. They meet and discuss making important changes for the future, which can give students a real voice within the nursing community.

If you take students from the very beginning they are more likely to be proud and to feel part of a massive organisation like the RCN later on, and that is something that certainly happened for me.

I think that is really important for young nurses to know that they are valued as a member, that they are respected as a nurse and that their

opinions really do matter. That is how young nurses feel in the RCN.

I think people don't come into nursing for money, they really don't. They come into it because they love their job, they love to care. That is why you have got to keep doing it.

Being a nurse to me is making a difference in somebody's life every single day. Knowing that what I do genuinely makes a positive difference in somebody's life – be it the patient, the families or my colleagues – that to me is an irreplaceable feeling.

RCN Wales is really proud of the work of its members. It respects its members. It gives members something that they cannot always get in work: that level of support of knowing that you as a nurse really do matter.

The RCN makes sure that nurses count and that nursing counts right at the forefront, right on the frontline.

Billy Nichols
Staff Nurse, RCN Wales Representative and RCN Welsh Board Member.

I had been teaching for a short period and I found that I didn't want to do that anymore, but I wanted to work in an environment where I was giving of myself so that is why I became a nurse.

Being a nurse is very tiring, heartbreaking sometimes, but at the end of the day it is very rewarding.

I would always encourage others who feel that tug towards nursing to go for it. Over my career I have continued to feel a sense of purpose, feeling that I have something to contribute to the population of the UK and Wales.

Over the past 50 years I think RCN Wales has played an important role in improving the working lives of nurses in Britain and Wales. A large proportion of the nursing workforce belongs to the RCN so we have done a lot of good for the workforce in general.

RCN Wales has many strengths, both in a professional aspect and also as a trade union, so we can represent our nursing colleagues in the nursing family in a knowledgeable way.

Members have access to the RCN website and the RCN library online. It is a great tool for professional development. Also, if you should get into trouble you are represented by a nurse who understands the issues rather than a generic trade union where you would be represented by other professional groups that do not necessarily understand your issue.

I think it is very important that the RCN works in conjunction with politicians to raise the standing of nurses and nursing in the UK and Wales. We are working really hard with the politicians and I think we are raising the standards.

Having an RCN organisation specific to Wales and a headquarters in Cardiff means we have a focus for members here, rather than being run from London and becoming London-centric which most other trade unions and professional bodies are.

RCN Wales supports nurses but it does not simply play a supporting role. It has also taken the lead in advocating for nurses and nursing on many issues, most recently and currently on the key issue of safe staffing levels.

Sue Grave

Staff Nurse, Winner, Nursing Student Award, RCN in Wales Nurse of the Year 2014.

I was put forward for the Student Nurse of the Year award by a tutor from Glyndwr University because of changes I had made in practice on my clinical placements at the Wrexham Maelor Hospital. For instance, I worked with a lady who was suffering from breast cancer but was also a victim of domestic violence. She talked to me about it and I felt like I had a duty to be able to sort something out for her, but I found that there were quite a few barriers to getting some domestic violence related counselling for her. I finally put her in touch with somebody and she got the help she needed. That gave me a great sense of achievement and of making a difference – and that's why I came into nursing.

I reflected on it and it was actually published in the Starting Out section of the RCN's Nursing Standard magazine. I have gone on to do another reflective account and I am now on their readers' panel, continuing to answer questions that are current issues.

The award means I can go on and do what I want to do. It has given me the confidence to be able to do it.

For me the Nurse of the Year ceremony is a celebration of everything about nursing. All credit to RCN Wales for recognising nurses in this way because on the evening just to be there with such inspirational people was amazing. For me, a student starting out on her career, it was fantastic to be around so many wonderful nurses.

I joined RCN Wales because I feel it is a body that understands nurses' issues and everything about the role of the nurse. It is a union to

support and encourage you, and to promote everything that is good about nursing.

Being a nurse is a vocation, certainly for me. I came into nursing as a mature student but it was something that had been at the back of my mind for as long as I can remember. I had never had the opportunity to do it for financial or other reasons. It is fantastic that now I have been able to fulfil my dream and that's what it means to me.

Nursing gives me that marvellous sense of making a difference, of working with people, especially the elderly, and being able to help them.

I love helping people so that just says it all for me.

Peter Meredith-Smith

Associate Director (Employment Relations), RCN in Wales.

Having initially trained as an actor at the Royal Welsh College of Music and Drama, I took a change in career direction and began my mental health nurse training at the Mid Glamorgan School of Nursing in Bridgend in June 1981. The School of Nursing subsequently became part of the University of Glamorgan, which has since been incorporated into the University of South Wales.

I completed my nurse training in 1984, becoming a Registered Mental Health Nurse in November of that year. Not long after registering I began studying for the University of Wales Diploma in Nursing.

At that time, before the era of graduate level preparation for a career in nursing in Wales, the Diploma in Nursing was 'the' foundation post-basic qualification for nurses seeking career development. During my studies for the Diploma I was part of what turned out to be quite a high flying group of students that included Jean White (the current Chief Nursing Officer for Wales) and Sir Jonathon Ashbridge

(the inaugural President of the Nursing and Midwifery Council). In 1988 I achieved my Master of Nursing Degree from the then University of Wales College of Medicine.

During my career I have had the great privilege of serving patients throughout Wales in all parts of the healthcare system: from bedside to Board level, at Government level and as part of the Royal College of Nursing. Throughout my clinical career I worked extensively in community and in-patient services, covering most clinical specialities in mental healthcare. I was lucky enough to work for over ten years for the Welsh Government as a Nursing Officer. Before then I had worked as Senior Lecturer in Swansea (running an MSc Nursing course and teaching on other nursing courses).

I have benefited from significant experience as an NHS Executive, having held two Clinical Directorships (I was one of the first non-medical Clinical Directors to be appointed in Wales in the 1990s). I have also held the position of Executive Nurse Director.

During my time studying at the Royal Welsh College of Music and Drama I was very politically active (I was President of the Student's Union), but more importantly I was very conscious of my social responsibilities. Consequently, thinking that seeking a career in acting was somewhat self-indulgent, I submitted to the streak of altruism that ran through me and applied to study to become a nurse.

I never wanted to be just any sort of nurse. I wanted to be a mental health nurse – and I've never regretted my decision to become one!

In my view, when properly supported to achieve all that it is capable of, the nursing profession, and the value ascribed to it by society, is one of civilised society's great achievements. I believe we should be prepared to do all that we can to protect the profession and to nurture and develop it for the benefit of society. We should never cease in our efforts to improve what nurses do for the patients and communities we serve.

*

I became a member of the RCN too long ago to remember! I joined because of the organisation's reputation for successfully working to protect and improve health services in Wales and for standing up for nurses.

The RCN in Wales is the premier professional association of nurses and trades union for nurses in Wales. It is the organisation that all significant healthcare stakeholders in Wales turn to when they need an informed legitimate view on any nursing issue.

In my role at the RCN in Wales I have various responsibilities. Firstly, I am a deputy to the Director of the RCN in Wales; secondly, I am the Deputy Secretary to the Welsh Board of the RCN; and finally I lead and manage the Trades Union service of the RCN in Wales.

As the RCN Welsh Management Team's lead for Employment Relations (and consequently a member of the NHS Wales National Partnership Forum), I am often part of the NHS Wales Trades Unions' senior negotiating team on all sort of issues relating to NHS Wales terms and conditions of employment. This involves negotiating at government level on issues that are very important to RCN members, such as pay and pay protection following organisational change.

My role involves me in many campaigns, often in partnership with other trades unions and the TUC. A memorable and heated campaign in recent years was the one that sought to protect NHS pensions.

I have no doubt that the influence of the RCN on Welsh Government is very significant, particularly under the leadership of Tina Donnelly

I have no doubt that the influence of the RCN on Welsh Government is very significant, particularly under the leadership of Tina Donnelly, the current Director of RCN Wales. She has forged an exceptionally productive relationship with not only the Welsh Government but with the leaders and health spokespersons of all the political parties in Wales.

*

As I am being interviewed for this contribution to the RCN in Wales' book to celebrate the 50th anniversary of the opening of Tŷ Maeth, health services in Wales have never before been under such pressure or at such risk.

Demand for services is escalating, resources in real terms are diminishing and nurses are being pushed harder than ever to make our health services work in what is an extremely challenging service environment.

The RCN in Wales must be seen to be 'here to stay' and to 'grow stronger year on year' so that it may continue to effectively look after our members' interest through these tough times and beyond.

Alison Davies
Associate Director (Professional Practice), RCN in Wales.

My life as a nurse has brought everything that a fantastic career could; it has been varied, diverse, interesting, challenging, engaging and developmental.

I've met many fantastic people during my career, working in North, Mid and South Wales as well as Cheshire. Having held a number of senior nursing posts and being appointed as one of the first Consultant Nurses in Wales, I've had the opportunity to travel the UK, enabling me to learn about health and health care in its broadest context.

As clichéd as it might sound, I believe nursing is a vocation and this is why I became a nurse: a want and need to work with and for people.

My role at RCN Wales is essentially about advocating for the enablers to be in place that support the nursing family in providing the highest standards of care in any setting to any person who needs it.

I've been a member of the RCN since 1982, when I became a student nurse. The reason I joined the RCN is the same reason I have maintained a long career in nursing, I truly believe in the difference nurses can make to people's lives when they are enabled and empowered to do so.

RCN Wales is a collection of highly-dedicated and talented individuals who work together for the good of our members along with the people who need and use health services in Wales. It is important that the RCN has a physical base in Wales in recognition of the devolved nature of health policy; establishing and maintaining a permanent presence in Wales brings opportunity to shape the national agenda and has measurable benefits, for example, the way in which the Nurse Staffing Levels (Wales) Bill has been supported and progressed. I believe in the future, this will be seen as an iconic campaign, the first of its kind in the UK with the promise of ground-breaking significance. This is one of a number of arenas where the reputation established by being in Wales and being highly conversant with the Welsh agenda makes all the difference.

As the people who are very aware of the difficulties faced in healthcare, as well as the possible solutions, it is imperative that nurses, midwives and healthcare support workers have the opportunity to directly influence policy-

makers, to influence and shape the strategic direction for Wales. RCN Wales proactively enables this exchange in a whole variety of ways. I think this is the factor that the credibility of the RCN in Wales springs from; it provides an excellent platform for members to get their message heard, where it can inform the future.

The challenges and opportunities faced by nurses and nursing as a profession are many and diverse. We need to be strong, to be heard and to be committed to making sure the people of Wales receive the highest standard of care and that the people providing it are enabled to do so. From my perspective, to be part of the solution is a privilege and an honour.

Ruth Owens

Ward Sister, Winner, Older Person's Commissioner for Wales Award 2013 and Winner, Nurse of the Year 2013.

My grandma was a nurse and she inspired me to do the same. She was very much a matron kind of figure. She was always very confident and made people feel better. If there was ever an accident or someone in the family was unwell she always seemed to be able to take control and make you feel safe. I also had an in-patient stay as a young child and unfortunately some of the nurses were not kind. I wanted to ensure I did better.

When you know you have made a difference it makes it all worthwhile; it makes the tough times worth it.

The award which I won – and which my grandma would have definitely have won if they had it in her day – was the Older Person's

Commissioner Award in 2013 and the overall Nurse of the Year. I was a Ward Sister in Barry Hospital, which is a small community hospital. I developed a really good team, with high standards of care and low sickness rates. It was a happy ward which was open to change and dedicated to continuing improving the standards of care that were being delivered.

When you are a student you are told that you need to join a union and it was not really until a few years into my nursing career that I thought I would join the RCN. It is a good place to go for guidance on professional issues and it is nice to feel like you are a member of something. It gives us someone outside our employer that we can talk to. It is a voice for nurses and within the college there are role models as well.

Being a nurse is challenging but it is rewarding. I have never known anything else so I cannot imagine doing anything else. It is something I think you are born to do.

We are going through a really tough time, and it might get a little bit harder but it will get better. We have got some fantastic nurses coming through. I have some students on the ward who I think are absolutely amazing. I think the future is bright but in the short term it is going to be really tough.

If in time my own granddaughter came to me and said she wanted to be a nurse I'd say that if she wanted it for the money I would not recommend it but if she wanted a rewarding career then definitely go for it.

When you know you have made a difference it makes it all worthwhile; it makes the tough times worth it.

Gaynor Jones

Staff Nurse, Chair of the RCN Welsh Board and
RCN Council Member for Wales.

I was late coming into nursing. I was already married with a young daughter, but it was something I wanted to do. My parents and my in-laws were very supportive and I started my training just before I was 30.

Becoming a nurse was a very proud moment for me. I was proud not just for myself but for my family. My father was the proudest person, I left school at 15 with no qualifications and did my SEN training first as it was only a two-year course and I was not really aware of the difference in the two levels of nursing, but here I was, this older person with a family, achieving what I always wanted to do.

I later completed the conversion course to become a first level nurse, which was another achievement for me.

I worked with a male charge nurse who was an RCN steward and he persuaded me to go along to an RCN branch meeting. I went along, never intending to do anything at all, but they needed a secretary and I was volunteered to do that!

Then I started taking on a little bit more work, then more work, until I now work 30 hours in my role as an RCN steward in my University Health Board and seven-and-a-half in my clinical shift at Accident and Emergency in Prince Charles Hospital in Merthyr Tydfil.

Being a steward is a superb role, very diverse: from attending meetings with HR to considering policies; from looking at procedures in the organisation to supporting and representing members in disciplinary meetings, and giving simple advice to members of staff. Sometimes it is just a colleague who passes you in the corridor and has a little question for you. All the work gives me a wonderful sense of satisfaction and achievement.

Members can get not just employment relations advice from the RCN but professional advice and guidance about education. The RCN has the largest nursing library in the world, so it offers many things for students, registered nurses and healthcare support workers.

The RCN is always making things better for nurses. If there is any bullying in the workplace then either the local RCN steward or someone from the employment relations team will go in to make sure we can make a better working environment for staff, which also improves things for patients.

I became Chair of the Welsh Board in 2013, and that was absolutely fantastic. The board meets four times a year and has a governance role so we look at issues affecting not just the RCN but

health boards, and we look at where we could influence and improve nurses' lives and the NHS. Our work has a major impact on members because we look at such things as why sickness levels might be high, why so many people are off with stress and what we can do to support them.

I am so proud to be Chair, I absolutely love it, not so much because of the role but because it has given me so much. It is difficult to explain but I sometimes think I can say what I do for the RCN – and I do a lot, perhaps 50 hours a week – but it is harder to describe what the RCN has done for me.

The RCN has given me the opportunities to meet people I would never have met: nurses across the whole of Wales and, of course, my RCN Council colleagues from across the UK. I have also had the opportunity to meet AMs, MPs, people from all walks of life, and to me

I still work on the shop floor because I choose to. I love working with patients.

that is fantastic. It has given me the confidence to get up on stage at political conferences – Labour and Conservative – and speak to all these politicians who are used to making speeches. It has given me the knowledge so that when I speak at these events that they can see what I am saying is important. I always find everyone to be very supportive and encouraging. I love talking about nurses and nursing and how we can support the patients in our care. Nurses have some fantastic ideas of how we can improve the care of the patients in Wales.

I am also the Welsh Government appointed Independent Board member on my health board. I represent all the trade unions and all the staff working in the Cwm Taf Health Board.

I still work on the shop floor because I choose to. I love working with patients. As much as I love representing the RCN and its members, I have the best of both worlds. I am a very lucky person.

*

The key issues at the moment are staffing levels and we have been campaigning very hard to have safe staffing on our wards. It is not just safe staffing, it is having the staff with the right knowledge and skills working in a specific area and I think that is important as well.

Our safe staffing campaign started with a joint idea by Kirsty Williams CBE AM and RCN Wales. It started off, I suppose, as something quite small but has developed into a campaign which is a very important for the RCN and which could have a real affect on the Welsh NHS.

In September, 2015, I had the privilege of launching the RCN 'Time to Care' campaign which was held at the Senedd and hosted by David Rees AM. It was really good to see so many AMs and nurses there talking about the care of patients in Wales in what ever area there were being cared for, and what we could all do to ensure that the care they were receiving was the best it possibly could be.

Another wonderful achievement for the RCN in Wales is that, thanks to Tina Donnelly, the Director, we have just held our fourth annual Nurse of the Year awards at the City Hall in Cardiff. This has become a very successful event, where we have the opportunity to celebrate all the wonderful work that is being undertaken by the nursing family across Wales.

The RCN makes its voice heard wherever there are people there to listen. In Wales that is the

Welsh Government, Members of the European Parliament, Board Chairs and Chief Executives. Wherever there is anybody to listen to us on how we can improve things for nurses and ultimately improve things for patients, the RCN is there and it speaks out.

*

The story of Tŷ Maeth is a wonderful one. It is absolutely fantastic to think that in 1965, when people were earning very little money, nurses went out, campaigned and fundraised to have a building for nurses in Wales. It is wonderful for us to be celebrating our 50th anniversary. It is a superb building and we are all so proud to be part of the history of Tŷ Maeth.

The RCN in Wales is professional, caring and supportive. Wales is a country in its own right and has to represent itself. We have things that are unique to Wales. We have a devolved government so we need to have somebody who can speak to the Welsh Government at the right level, to ensure the right message gets over to make life better, not just for the staff, but for the patients – for the people of Wales.

RCN in Wales at work

RCN Wales is both a trade union and a professional body. It represents members, giving support, advice and protection, and provides education and training.

RCN Wales has a rich history of campaigning for better lives for nurses and patients. As it celebrates its 50th anniversary, RCN Wales is the most important and influential nursing organisation in the country.

It now has 134 representatives looking after the needs and concerns of 25,000 members across Wales.

In the 1980s RCN Wales championed the cause of research in nursing and funded a Chair of Nursing Research. It later supported the move to take nurse and midwife education to degree level.

It is proud of the diversity of its members and is dedicated to inclusion.

RCN Wales has always campaigned right to the heart of government. Since devolution RCN Wales has been able to speak up even more powerfully for the nursing profession.

For the past few years it has been campaigning for safe staffing levels in the Welsh NHS. This became subject of a Bill – now called the Nurse Staffing Levels (Wales) Bill – at the National Assembly for Wales.

Retired RCN member Richard Jones MBE submitted an e-petition on the Assembly website which garnered 1,579 signatures.

RCN Wales believes this new law would greatly improve patient safety and provide patients with the nursing care and attention they deserve. The Bill will put a legal requirement onto health boards to ensure that there are an adequate number of registered nurses on a ward.

The Bill is now making its way through the Assembly process. Safe staffing and support for the Bill is central to RCN Wales's Time to Care 2016 political manifesto for the Assembly elections.

Royal visits to Tŷ Maeth

KENSINGTON PALACE
W8 4PU

    I congratulate the Royal College of Nursing, Welsh Board, on the 30th Anniversary of its Headquarters in Wales - Ty Maeth.

    This is my third visit to Ty Maeth, having formally opened the building in 1965, and then, in 1983, to commemorate the extension of the Harry Gibson Suite. I hear the contribution to patient care being made by nurses and nursing in the Principality is excellent and I extend my best wishes to you all on the occasion of the 30th anniversary and for your continued success.

Patron
Royal College of Nursing

26th October, 1995

HRH Princess Margaret visits to celebrate the 30th anniversary of Tŷ Maeth.

In 2005 Princess Anne visited to mark the 40th anniversary of Tŷ Maeth.

Beverly Malone, RCN General Secretary and Her Royal Highness

RCN Wales Director
Liz Hewett

'Value Nursing' campaign

In 2003 RCN Wales took its 'Value Nursing' campaign to the National Assembly for Wales. The campaign was led by RCN Wales Director Liz Hewett.

Members were met by a number of assembly members including Ieuan Wyn Jones, of Plaid Cymru, Kirsty Williams CBE, of the Liberal Democrats, and Labour's Jane Hutt, who was then Health Minister for Wales.

'Get it Right' campaign

In September 2007 RCN Wales launched its 'Get It Right' campaign, which provided key policy briefings to Assembly Members on the top health issues the Welsh nursing family wanted the National Assembly for Wales to address.

The campaign would last for three years. Successes included the introduction of a national school nurse strategy and a substantial increase in community nursing numbers.

The 'Free to Lead, Free to Care' ward sister initiative led to improvements in patient care in hydration, nutrition and communication.

These photographs are from the launch of the third year of the campaign and were taken at the National Assembly in November 2009.

The event was attended by Assembly Members from all parties and around 50 RCN members from across Wales.

The RCN Wales team at the Assembly in 2009 was led by Board Chair Dave Williams; Tina Donnelly, RCN Wales Director; and Lisa Turnbull, Policy and Public Affairs Adviser.

Above: Tina Donnelly, Director RCN in Wales , with Lorraine Barratt AM.

Right top: Edwina Hart MBE AM, Minister for Health and Social Services (centre) at the 2008 campaign launch with (left) RCN Deputy Director Richard Jones and RCN Director Tina Donnelly and (right) Board Chair Gareth Phillips and Val Lloyd AM.

Right bottom: Director Tina Donnelly and Deputy Director Richard Jones chat with Jenny Randerson AM (now The Baroness Randerson).

Above: Neil Evans, William Graham AM, Lynne Vincent.

Page 84, top: RCN members pose for a photograph with Dai Lloyd AM.

Page 84, bottom: Another trip to the Senedd: RCN Chair Eirlys Warrington (centre with chain of office) leads RCN members to the steps of the Assembly in 2007 with the 'Nursing Matters' Campaign.

Inaugural Nurse of the Year 2012

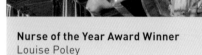

Nurse of the Year Award Winner
Louise Poley

Nursing Student Award Winner
Georgina Hobson

Nursing Student Award Runner Up
Anthony Green

Health Care Support Worker Award Winner
Tracey Davies

**Health Care Support Worker Award
Runner Up**
Claire Smith

Clinical Nurse Specialist Award Winner
Nicola West

Clinical Nurse Specialist Award Runner Up
Vicki Myson

Children & Midwifery Award Joint Winner
Maureen Jones

Children & Midwifery Award Joint Winner
Irfon Williams

Chief Nursing Officer for Wales Award Winner
Tanya Strange

Chief Nursing Officer Award Runner Up
Jill Galvani

Mental Health & Learning Disabilities Award Winner
Louise Poley

Mental Health & Learning Disabilities Award Runner Up
Sali Burns

**Registered Nurse (Adult) Award Winner
and Nurse of the Year Runner Up**
Lisa Franklin

Registered Nurse (Adult) Award Runner Up
Jenny Anne Buckley

**Research and Innovation Nursing Award
Winner**
Phedra Dodds

**Research and Innovation Nursing Award
Runner Up**
Liz Waters

Community Nursing Award Winner
Jane Brunsdon

Community Nurse Award Runner Up
Liz Howlett

Nurse of the Year 2013

Nurse of the Year Awards 2013

Nurse of the Year Award Winner
Ruth Owens

Lifetime Achievement Award Winner
Helen Bennett

Humanitarian Relief Award Winner
Melrose East

Humanitarian Relief Award Runner Up
Terri Levett

Nursing Student Award Winner
Caitlin Rhiannon Griffiths

Nursing Student Award Runner Up
Lauren Cross

Health Care Support Worker Award Winner
The General Surgery, Urology, Head & Neck
Quality Standards Group

**Health Care Support Worker Award
Runner Up**
David Lomas

Clinical Nurse Specialist Award Winner
Petula Garner

Clinical Nurse Specialist Award Runner Up
Jane Whittingham

**Mental Health & Learning Disabilites
Award Winner**
Andy Lodwick

**Mental Health & Learning Disabilities
Award Runner Up**
Emma-Jayne Hagerty

Children & Midwifery Award Winner
Glan y Mor Community Midwife Team

Children & Midwifery Award Runner Up
Leanne Thomas

Chief Nursing Officer for Wales Award Winner
Helen Dinham

Chief Nursing Officer for Wales Award Runner Up
Claire Williams

Innovation In Nursing Award Winner
Jane Whittingham

Innovation In Nursing Award Runner Up
Paula Jeffrey

Community Nursing Award Winner
Lorraine Handicott

Community Nursing Award Runner Up
Anne Gibby

Older People's Commissioner for Wales Award
Ruth Owens

Older People's Commissioner for Wales Award Runner Up
Sian Brooks

Nurse Education Award Winner
Wendy Pugh

Nurse Education Award Runner Up
Rachel Hart

Research In Nursing Award Winner
Carolyn Middleton

Research In Nursing Award Runner Up
Sue Francombe

Registered Nurse (Adult) Award Winner
Julie Brown

Nurse of the Year 2014

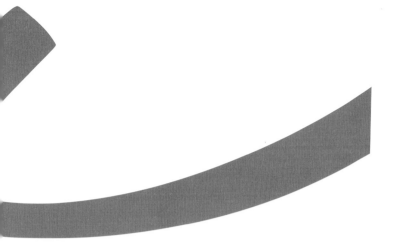

Nurse of the Year Awards 2014

Nurse of the Year Award Winner
Veronica Jarman

Lifetime Achievement Award Winner
Daphne Meredith-Smith

Humanitarian Relief Award Winner
Ann-Marie Ablett

Humanitarian Relief Award Runner Up
Kath Smith

Nursing Student Award Winner
Sue Grave

Nursing Student Award Runner Up
Anitha Uddin

Health Care Support Worker Award Winner
Bethan Turner

Health Care Support Worker Award Runner Up
Lisa Morgan

Clinical Nurse Specialist Award Winners
Delyth Tomkinson & Tara Rees

Clinical Nurse Specialist Award Runner Up
Lynne Greenhill

Mental Health & Learning Disabilities Award Winner
Karen Bracegirdle

Mental Health & Learning Disabilities Award Runner Up
Matthew Reynolds

Children & Midwifery Award Winner
Adele Roberts

Children & Midwifery Award Runner Up
Kath Maguire

Registered Nurse (Adult) Award Winner
Louise Rooney

Registered Nurse (Adult) Award Runner Up
Kathleen Farr

Innovation In Nursing Award Winner
Wayne Parsons

Innovation in Nursing Award Runner Up
Lisa Cordery

Community Nursing Award Winner
Teresa Evans

Community Nursing Award Runner Up
Ana Llewellyn

Older People's Commissioner for Wales Award Winner
Veronica Jarman

Older People's Commissioner for Wales Award Runner Up
Vicki Broad

Nurse Education Award Winner
Ann Richards

Nurse Education Award Runner Up
Caroline Whittaker

Research In Nursing Award Winner
Professor Lesley Lowes

Research In Nursing Award Runner Up
Nicola West

**Chief Nursing Officer for Wales Award
Joint Winners**
Jane Hart & Jane Randall

Nurse of the Year 2015

Nurse of the Year Awards 2015

Nurse of the Year Award Winner
Claire Harris

Lifetime Achievement Award
Brenda Scourfield

Humanitarian Nursing Award Winner
Roisin O'Hare

Humanitarian Nursing Award Runner Up
Emily Brace

Nursing Student Award Winner
Steffan Robbins

Nursing Student Award Runner Up
Jade Silver

Health Care Support Worker Award Winner
Justine Jamieson

Health Care Support Worker Award Runner Up
Karen Williams

Clinical Nurse Specialist Award Winner
Emily Carne

Clinical Nurse Specialist Award Runner Up
Richard Jones

Mental Health & Learning Disabilities Award Winner
Tracey Lloyd

Mental Health & Learning Disabilities Award Runner Up
Lisa Kinsella

Children & Midwifery Award Winners
Helen Erasmus & Liz Smith

Children & Midwifery Award Runner Up
Marita Fernandez

Chief Nursing Officer for Wales Award Winner
Claire Harris

Chief Nursing Officer for Wales Award Runners Up
Dr Carolyn Middleton & Dr Nicola Ryley

Registered Nurse (Adult) Award Winner
Debbie Davies

Registered Nurse (Adult) Award Runner Up
Lisa Marshall

Innovation In Nursing Award Winner
Sarah Ann Beuschel

Innovation In Nursing Award Runner Up
Bethan Lewis

Community Nursing Award Winners
Ann Bamsey & Susan Grounds

Community Nursing Award Runner Up
Richard Desir

Older People's Commissioner for Wales Award Winner
Arleen Testa

Older People's Commissioner for Wales Award Runner Up
Christopher Sayer

Nurse Education Award Winner
Dr Malcolm Godwin

Nurse Education Award Runner Up
Alison Kirton

Research In Nursing Award Winner
Dr Ben Hannigan

Research In Nursing Award Runner Up
Professor Christopher Burton

**Improving Individual & Population Health
Award Winner**
Kath Goode

**Improving Individual & Population Health
Award Runner Up**
Anne Thomas

Tŷ Maeth, 50 Glorious Years

By Fiona Johnson,
Director of Communications, RCN

Tŷ Maeth, Tŷ Maeth, 50 glorious years,
Built by our members, with blood, sweat and tears;
Three hundred thousand was raised for the Board
At modern day prices, a six million pound hoard!
It's your place of learning, it's your house of nurture,
Be proud of its past and be part of its future.

Christine and Gaynor, Gaynor and Christine,
The make up's immaculate, the dresses are pristine;
More to the point, members be in no doubt,
They'll fight for your interests, day in and day out;
If you quibble and fudge things, they won't be impressed,
The patients of Wales deserve only the best.

You've made safe nurse staffing your number one aim,
With grit and persistence you'll win the campaign;
Elections are looming, all parties please note,
If you don't back our nurses, you won't get their vote!
From Bangor to Blaenau, to Penrhydeudraeth,
Dolgellau and Merthyr and back to Tŷ Maeth;
From Colwyn to Cardiff and on to Tredegar,
Burning the miles in her bright orange sports car,
I am sure you'll agree that there's never been a
Better champion for nursing than Wilma Christina.

The members all know her from TV and wireless,
Her media profile is sky high and fearless,
She's very at home in the Cardiff Bay bubble,
For AMs and ministers Tina means trouble,
Don't cross her, don't vex her, or you'll soon be cursing,
She will prevail with her passion for nursing.

She'll weigh up the evidence, reach her decision,
The campaign approach: military precision.
She's a leader, a soldier and for better or worse,
First, last and always, Tina's a nurse.

RCN in Wales Nurse of
the Year Awards 2015

The health care support worker, the midwife, the nurse,
Your talents are many, your skills are diverse.
Our students, their teachers – the future is bright;
It's time to say thank you with this gala night.
To all of our finalists, you've done nursing proud,
Tonight we salute you with cheers long and loud.

Ladies and gentlemen, colleagues and friends,
My affectionate tribute is nearing its end.
There'll be cheering and clapping, you may shed a tear,
As we move to announce our new Nurse of the Year.
For all of our members, whose strength never fails,
Please lift up your glasses... to RCN Wales!

Fiona Johnson

Photo credits

Back cover images: © RCN Wales Archive.
© Stuart Fisher: Pages 4, 6, 29, 49, 50, 52, 60, 66, 68, 69, 70, 71, 72, 73, 75, 76, 77, 94-97, 98-101, 102-105, 106-107, 108-109, 110-114, 115, 116-119, 120-124, 125, 127.
© RCN Wales Archive: Pages 8-11, 12-17, 18, 20, 22, 23 (top), 24, 26, 31, 34-41, 44, 54, 58, 64, 78, 79 (top), 80-85, 86-89, 90-93.
© Tina Donnelly: Page 28.
© Clare Bruce: Pages 30, 33, 46, 47, 48.
© Paul Roberts: Pages 23, 42, 55, 62, 74.
© Gareth Thomas: Page 65.
© Sarah Barnes: Page 67.
© Greg Lewis: Pages 76, 79 (middle and bottom).
Timeline photos (Pages 8-11): 1959-1998, 2005 © RCN Wales Archive; 2004, 2012-2015 © Stuart Fisher; Time to Care, © Sarah Barnes.

Every effort has been made to trace copyright holders of material and acknowledge permission for this publication. The publisher apologises for any errors or omissions to rights holders and would be grateful for notification of credits and corrections that should be included in future reprints or editions of this book.

Greg Lewis would like to thank Collin Games, Paul Roberts, Gareth Thomas and Peter Eveson for their work on the film which inspired this book; Joana Rodrigues, of Graffeg, for her work on its design; and Tina Donnelly and the staff of RCN Wales for their co-operation in the making of the film and the book.